BEFORE THE RAINBOW

1st Edition

Published in 2016 by

Woodfield Publishing Ltd
Bognor Regis PO21 5EL England
www.woodfieldpublishing.co.uk

ISBN 1-84683-173-7

Printed and bound in England

Typesetting & page design: Nic Pastorius
Cover design: Klaus Schaffer

Source document
Before the Rainbow by Joan Blackburn (final)

Before the Rainbow

The story of Charles & Alice, 1901-41

JOAN BLACKBURN

Joan Blackburn.
(nee Ratcliff)

Woodfield

Woodfield Publishing Ltd

Bognor Regis ~ West Sussex ~ England ~ PO21 5EL
tel 01243 821234 ~ **e/m** info@woodfieldpublishing.co.uk

Interesting and informative books on a variety of subjects

For full details of all our published titles, visit our website at
www.woodfieldpublishing.co.uk

Contents

INTRODUCTION...VII

I. Pitsford, Northamptonshire, 1901.............................ix

II. Belton House, Grantham, 1901.................................11

III. Easthampstead Park, 1901.......................................31

IV. Big Changes, 1906..43

V. The Right One...56

VI. Wedding Bells, 1908..68

VII. Haywards Heath, 1908-15..76

VIII. Redhill, 1914...87

IX. 'The Bit in Between' 93

X. The Beginning of the End.....................................124

XI. Chailey Green, 1915..131

XII. Chapter Twelve Big Changes, 1918......................141

XIII. Coxhill Manor, Chobham 1920.............................149

XIV. The End of an Era, 1929..163

XV. Dark Days, 1929..176

XVI. Before the Rainbow, 1937......................................191

EPILOGUE...212

ABOUT THE AUTHOR...216

This book is dedicated to these six people.
'The salt of the earth'

*John &
Elizabeth
Ratcliff*

*Charles Ratcliff
& Alice Jones*

*Joshua Kirck Jones
& Sarah Jones*

Introduction

Charles Ratcliff, a country boy from Northamptonshire, started his working life (along with his friend Henry Winters) as a gardener's boy in the Bothy at Althorp House. At the same time Alice Jones, a 'townie' from Barnes, on the edge of London, served as Parlour Maid at the estate of Lord Normanton at Ringwood in Hampshire and then moved to Easthampstead Park, the country home of the Marquess of Downshire.

This book follows Alice and Charles as they move from place to place and eventually meet. It then follows them through the agonies of the First World War, when Charles, the gardener, found himself a soldier in the West Surrey Regiment fighting on The Somme while Henry, who had returned to Manchester with his new wife, ended up in the Lancashire Fusiliers, fighting in the Dardanelles and eventually being taken prisoner.

Against a backdrop of some of the most prestigious country estates in England, it follows their lives and those of their families from the death of Queen Victoria in 1901 until the Battle of Britain in 1941.[1]

It is Alice and Charles's story. All of it is true and, with the exception of a few minor characters, all names are real. The conversations are, of course, imagined but are based on the author's knowledge of the people concerned.

Joan Blackburn, April 2016.

---

[1] THIS MAY SEEM a strange place to stop but the story is continued in *Granddad's Rainbow* which reveals what happened to the various members of the Ratcliff family during the remainder of World War II and afterwards. J.B.

The Peace Rose.

CHAPTER I

Pitsford, Northamptonshire, 1901

The sound of the cockerel clearing his throat in the nearby farm woke Elizabeth Ratcliff from her sleep. She lay for a while, as her eyes accustomed themselves to the faint light that was starting to push away the blackness of night. She lay still because she didn't want to wake up her husband John who seemed to be 'out to the world' beside her. But it was for only a few minutes and the cockerel, as if finding a second wind, let out an almighty crow at twice the volume of the previous one. John rolled over in bed and sat up.

"Dang thing, one of these days I will wring its neck, I swear I will."

Elizabeth grinned to herself. It was the same routine, every morning. Every morning he moaned about the bird but he needed to get up anyway. It was 5 am on a spring morning in the year 1901 and there were jobs to do. Many of the residents of the village of Pitsford in Northamptonshire would already be out and about. It was a farming area and time was of the essence. Elizabeth went downstairs and put the kettle on the kitchen range to warm some water for washing. Her husband banged on their son's bedroom door oblivious to his three daughters sleeping in the next room, or trying to!

"Come on young man, show a leg!"

Elizabeth felt a lump come to her throat. There should be three sons in that room really, but her children were fleeing the nest and suddenly she felt very middle aged. Their eldest son, Joseph, was training as a baker and living as a boarder with a large family in Northampton. He was twenty-one now and she had to accept grudgingly that he had to spread his wings. Indeed he was courting a very nice young lady and she visualised that there might be a wedding in the air before long. However, she felt much more apprehensive about her youngest son Charles. He was only seventeen and, much to her disappointment, he had moved to Lincolnshire.

She poured the hot water into the sink as John arrived to have a wash and trim his beard but her mind was on young Charles, her 'baby boy' as she tried to accept that he was grown up now. He'd had a good job for the past three years working in the gardens of nearby Althorp House. Earl Spencer – or the 'Red Earl' as everyone called him because of his red beard – was a good employer and Charles had lived in the Bothy with other boys and just come home once a week on his day off. But, like many headstrong youngsters he wanted to spread his wings and, influenced by his older friend Henry and the offer of, what he thought, was a better position by the Agency, he had proceeded to a job working for the Brownlow family in Lincolnshire.

"But Mother, Henry is going and he will look out for me," Charles had said. "I want to see a bit more of England than just Pitsford and the Agency have said that I am capable."

There had been no stopping him once he became seventeen and that was only a couple of weeks ago back in April. Now it was May and she had already received a letter from him reassuring her that he was all right and being well looked after.

"I wonder how Charles is doing today!" she said out loud as she stirred the porridge on the range.

"Damn silly lad!" grumbled John "he had a good job there at Althorp. I just hope he knew what he was doing, that's all. Things will change now that Queen Victoria has died and these large country estates will have to work hard to survive. He could find himself out on his ear with this new job – last in and first out!"

He was right, of course. Things would not be the same and the country was in limbo at the moment. The old Queen died back in January and the Coronation of Edward the seventh was due to take place next year. It was well known though that he was overweight and prone to all sorts of illnesses. One couldn't help feeling that things would be changing now that the Victorian age was over. Not least the Ratcliff household.

"We can't baby him any more Elizabeth" said John. "You know our son as I do. He will do what he wants to do."

She looked over to the dresser in the corner where Charles had left his accordion or 'squeezebox' as he called it. She would miss that. He had learnt how to play one, as a child, when he had accompanied her to Salvation Army meetings. Back then he could not get his hands around it and she used to help him while he learnt which buttons to press with his fingers. Later on they had bought him one of his own and once he had grown he would often entertain the family with the music when he was home. It was a jolly time whenever he came home from Althorp House. She could play it, of course, but that wasn't the same. There was nothing like hearing your child playing the instrument even if there were a few bad notes and John covered his ears in mock horror. It always ended in laughter. She picked it up and covered it in a cloth and put it away in the cupboard.

"Well I shall look forward to a few tunes from Charles on that again," she said.

"He is a big boy now Elizabeth," repeated John.

"I know, I know!" she replied. "One day they will all be gone and then it will be just us."

"Now, there's a thought!" laughed John. "How quiet it would be without the girls and their chattering and him and that damn squeezebox"

It was quite light now and Elizabeth sat in her chair and watched as their middle son, 'young John', rushed downstairs and quickly helped himself to some porridge. The two men, one aged forty-three and the other nineteen, settled down together to eat.

"Don't bolt it boy!" chided John senior "you will get indigestion!"

Elizabeth was just anxious that they get on their way to their respective jobs. She had her three girls to get off to school yet, and a day of lace making lay ahead. She made it for a living and she could not get on with that until they were all out of the house. She put some more water on the range to warm up and then left the men to get on with their chat whilst she went upstairs to the girls who were already arguing over what to wear.

"Come on you three, stop your bickering and get ready for school." Yes, it would be quiet without them!

The three girls were so alike, all dark haired and with trim figures, although little six year old Mabel was inclined to podginess. The eldest Rosa, or Rose as her mother called her, was nearly fourteen and due to leave school soon. It was already intended that she would train to be a dressmaker. Then there was eight year old Emily who was the mischief maker of the family. However, they were a bit of a worry. Always ill for one reason or another and Elizabeth feared the continuous outbreaks of TB that seemed to go around. She tried to protect them as much as she could, but so much could be picked up from others at school. Much to their disgust, she quite often smeared goose fat onto brown paper and rubbed it on their chests and back in order to relieve it. Rose was already coughing. It was probably just a spring cold but Elizabeth was very wary of any sign of weakness in the chest. She knew of so many families who had lost youngsters to TB and it always seemed to be girls.

"Come on!" Elizabeth repeated. "I shouldn't have to chase you any more. You are big girls now." She turned to little Mabel. "Make sure you clean your teeth young lady, there is some powder in the closet. Rose! You take a spoonful of goose fat to make that cough better."

She left them to it and hurried off to see the men off to work. Her husband as a Stockman on the farm just down the road, which also housed the dreaded cockerel, whilst young John went off to his work as a Gardener on one of the large estates. Everyone worked hard in the Ratcliff household. John had been on the farms for most of his life, although, much to his wife's amusement, he did start out training to be an umbrella maker! Elizabeth giggled to herself at the thought. She could no more imagine John Charles making umbrellas any more than she could imagine pigs flying through the air like birds. It had been the idea of his Uncle James. It was an idea that had probably been carried out with the best of intentions at the time because his father, Joseph, had died at the impossibly young age of just thirty-one leaving his mother, Alice, devastated and with three small children – John Charles and his two sisters, Edna and Lucy. He had been just six years old when his Uncle took him away and, when he was old enough, placed him in lodgings with the Umbrella maker by the name of Mr. James Bull. Elizabeth knew that by the time her husband was fourteen he had been training to be a Cloth Dresser. She didn't know all the details, nor did she know much about cloth dressing, but clearly he felt that it was his duty to be with his mother and two sisters and so, when he was old enough he went back to

Pitsford. *"Good job too,"* she thought *"or I would never have met him and my children and future generations would not exist."*

She gave her husband and son a kiss and sent them on their way. Much as she loved them, all she wanted to do now was get them off to work and then concentrate on her chores before settling down to her lace making while there was plenty of outside light at the front of the house. The lace was much in demand by the gentry and, indeed, it was well known that some of it had made its way to the bedrooms of Queen Victoria. She was aroused from her thoughts by the girls falling over each other to get down the stairs.

"Mother! Emily has stolen my ribbons!" cried Rose. They were just in time to see their father and brother go out of the door.

"Emily, give them back to Rose right now!" snapped Elizabeth, "or you will go off to school without any breakfast inside you." She didn't mean it of course, but it was enough to get the ribbons back and for Emily to find her place at the table while Rose helped little Mabel.

"Goodbye father! Goodbye John!" called Rose behind the retreating figures.

Elizabeth could not help wondering again how Charles and Henry were getting on. The house was certainly less hectic without him and Joseph. At least with Joseph she would see him on his day off once a week but she didn't know when on earth she would see her youngest son again. He seemed quite happy to go wherever the Employment Agency sent him and she wouldn't put it past him to end up in the north of Scotland or the south of England.

"Oh shut up you silly old woman!" she silently scolded herself "Lincolnshire is not that far away!"

She busied herself clearing up and around the girls and washed the pots. It was a clear day outside so she would sit out there to make her lace. She always did so, if she could, as her eyesight was not as good as it used to be and she would rather have the daylight than the gas lamp. Moreover she was well known by the villagers of Pitsford and there was always somebody to stop and talk to her.

Finally, the girls were ready and dressed up in their smart gingham dresses and buttoned boots. It was eight thirty and Elizabeth felt as though she had been up for a week!

"At last!" she exclaimed. "Come on, get on your way!"

She gave each one a kiss and waved as they ran down the road. She stood and watched until they were quite out of sight and, once again, marvelled at the vagaries of life in general. How one second's decision in one generation can so influence everything in the next and beyond.

Now it was time to get her chair and all her equipment which consisted of her 'pillow' which was a cushion stuffed hard with straw and covered with a cloth for the lace to lie on with the bobbins hanging over the side. There could be anything from twenty to five hundred bobbins depending on the size of the item that was being made. Elizabeth also had her bobbin bag and her scissors dangling from the side of the pillow and also a pin cushion. All her pins were made of brass and most were very fine but with some heavier ones for the coarser lace. The bobbins were of wood with coloured beads on the end for the weight. The patterns were called  'The Fan', 'The Running River' and the 'Spider' and she was expert at them all. The designs were pricked out on a strip of parchment and great pride was taken in the pillows and the bobbins.

Of course she could have done her lace making in one of the many establishments that were provided in the Northampton area but it was much more convenient to do it at home and one didn't have the expense of paying for the room and the lighting.

Ten years ago The Midland Lace Association had been set up under the patronage of the Countess Spencer to improve the local manufacture of lace and also to improve the facilities for the workers. Elizabeth felt that her profession owed a lot to that lady as it was still a skill which was very much sought after and the income it made certainly helped to put bread on the table. John worked hard and long hours but his pay was not good. She thought of Joseph. Being the oldest boy, they had insisted that he did an apprenticeship and she was well satisfied that he would be a skilled baker. After all, one thing that everybody would need both now and in the future was bread. People could do without lace but they could never do without bread.

Elizabeth put on her starched white apron which was the trade mark of a good lace maker and then looked up at the sky to check for rain clouds. Satisfied, she settled herself down for the day. She found herself remembering when she had first gone to Lace School. She smiled to herself. She was getting it comparatively easy now compared to what it was like for youngsters back in the eighteen eighties. She had started at the age of six and it was quite normal to work ten hours per day with a half day on Saturday for one shilling a week. Yes, the lace makers of Northamptonshire owed the Countess Spencer a great deal for her patronage.

"Hello Elizabeth, how are you today?" She looked up to see the familiar sight of her neighbour, Margaret Steele. "Have you heard from that son of yours yet?"

"Yes Maggie" Elizabeth replied "he seems to be all right. I had a nice letter from him and he is living in the Bothy on an estate in Lincolnshire."

"Oh well my dear, I suppose they have to spread their wings at some time."

"Oh I know, but it was still a wrench to see him go." She carried on deftly making her lace while she spoke. "He is a good boy but can be hot headed."

"What about the meeting tonight?" Margaret went on. "Are you coming to the Salvation Army meeting? I do so love the music."

"Oh yes, I wouldn't miss it for the world."

Elizabeth and most of her extended family belonged to the up and coming Salvation Army and she and Margaret sang every week at the Mission Hall. Also, wherever possible, she went round helping to sell the "War Cry" to the local people. It had been set up some fifty years ago by William Booth in order to help the poor in the big cities but it had really caught on locally and she loved her smart navy and maroon uniform which she wore on 'high days and holidays' with the smart bonnet. John though, continued stoically to favour his local Parish Church but the couple supported each other.

"You haven't got John to take up the trumpet or the drum yet then Elizabeth?"

"No!" she laughed, "not John, he said he doesn't like all that 'happy clappy' stuff – he prefers "There is a Green Hill Far Away".

"Well, so do I" replied Margaret "I like both!"

"Oh well, at least he puts up with the rest of us banging our tambourines and selling the War Cry" laughed Elizabeth, and he suffered while Charles was learning the accordion.

Margaret came and peered over the gate to get a closer look at the lace that Elizabeth was deftly producing while she spoke. "You are so clever my dear!"

"Oh years of practice," she replied, "years of practice!"

"Well, I suppose I must get going." She picked up her basket from where she had placed it on the ground and bid her farewells. "I'll have to see if I can get some decent beef from old Thomas the butcher, it was really tough last time." With that she was gone and Elizabeth carried on with her lace making. She knew though that it would not be for long. One of the joys of sitting outside was the fact that she was never short of company for long just so long as they didn't mind her concentrating on her skills while she was talking.

She sat for about half an hour with just the sound of the birds for company but then she became aware of another familiar figure approaching. Her mother-in-law!

"Oh good lord" she thought to herself" no peace for the wicked!" Actually she did get on quite well with John's mother Alice and had a great deal of time for her. It must have been such a blow to have lost her husband when he was just thirty-one. Now she was in her sixties and had failing eyesight. She too had earned her living with lace making but since her eyesight had started to fail she had to give it up and now worked in the laundry. It was a hard and thankless job.

Alice stopped and leaned over the gate and Elizabeth thought ruefully that she had certainly aged since working in the laundry. She would have liked to have asked her in and given her a cup of tea but she knew that she was on her way to work and time was money. Of course the children had long since been off hand but she still had herself to keep.

"How are those grandchildren of mine?" she said "and how is Charles?, have you heard from him?"

"They are fine Alice" replied Elizabeth, "except that young Rose has a nasty cough." "As to Charles, well I think he is a 'chip off the old block' and he is making his own way and doing what he wants to do."

The older lady came forward and fingered the lacework.

"I'll have to pass on my pillow and bobbins to you or to the girls" she said "they are no good to me anymore. The eyes are not what they used to be."

Elizabeth didn't have time to answer before Alice was asking more questions.

"How are John and Pleasant my dear?" she said as she picked up her bag again. "Keeping well I hope?"

John and Pleasant Howard were Elizabeth's parents and they lived in Thornborough which was further south in Buckinghamshire. Consequently she didn't see as much of them as she would like to have done although they did keep in touch by letter and visited by train two or three times a year. They owned their own land and ran quite a successful farm which kept them both very busy all year round.

"They keep going," she replied, "it would take a lot to make them stop. The farm keeps them so busy." She smiled to herself when she thought of her mother and father. They had been good parents and had worked hard for her to go to the Lace School. They worked long hours and they expected their children to do the same. In fact Pleasant always said "if you can't make it or grow it my dear, then it is not worth having."

"That's good news Elizabeth," said Alice, feeling a slight hint of envy. She knew that they were hard workers but they'd had each other all their lives. She, herself, had never quite got over the death of her husband and the repercussions to her and her family, not least the sending away of young John. All had come out right in the end but she would always feel that slight degree of guilt. She remembered meeting her son's in-laws at his wedding to Elizabeth and thought what a nice couple they were.

"I always thought what a nice name that was," she said, as she gave Elizabeth a kiss on the cheek and parted company. "Pleasant by name and pleasant by nature."

With those words she was gone, rushing down the road to the Laundry. She didn't have to work the hours these days but even so, time was money and she wanted to be independent as long as she could.. Time was money to Elizabeth as well so she settled down to her work. Life in the little village of Pitsford, in the shadow of Althorp House, went on uninterrupted.

Althorp House – ancestral home of 'the Red Earl'.

CHAPTER II

Belton House, Grantham, 1901

A young blackbird perched on a nearby upturned bucket and watched Charles Ratcliff as he planted lettuces in straight lines in the kitchen garden. The seventeen-year-old stood up and stretched his back.

"I know what you are after!" he said. "Some nice, big, fat, juicy worms." He stood and surveyed his handiwork while the little creature just watched and waited for him to move out of the way. Charles wondered at just how many lettuces were needed for this household because he seemed to have been planting all afternoon and he was pretty deft at the job, marking the lines off with cotton to make it straight and then using a 'dibber' to cut the holes for the young seedlings to drop into easily. Now it was just a job of watering them in and he could finish for the day. He looked up at the sun and calculated that it must be at least six o'clock and high time that he was making his way back to the Bothy for some dinner. He did miss his mother's cooking but he certainly didn't starve and Belton House had some good cooks.

He had been here for three weeks now and just starting to get used to the place. It helped having his friend Henry with him as they had worked together at Althorp House. Lord Spencer, or 'the Red Earl' as everyone called him, had been a good employer and it had been exciting to work for someone so prestigious. Quite often he had seen carriages arrive carrying the gentry, and he knew that Mr. William Gladstone used to visit there regularly back in the 1890s.

Now he was at Belton House and it seemed to be just as 'posh'. He had already learned about his employer from the Chief Gardener.

"Oh he is quite somebody," Albert Horrocks said to him when he and Henry first arrived. "His full name is Adelbert Brownlow-Cust."

"Cor!" laughed Henry, "that's a mouthful."

Charles had been impressed. Apparently he was an old soldier and had been in the Grenadier Guards. Like Lord Spencer, he also mixed with Royalty and, until her death, had been Aide-de-Camp to Queen Victoria.

"I wouldn't mind doing a bit of soldiering myself," mused Henry. "It is a good way to see the world and get paid at the same time."

"The wife's name is just as much of a mouthful," went on Albert, ignoring Henry and his 'dreams'. "She is Lady Chelwynd Talbot."

Charles was impressed but he didn't think he would remember it. All he wanted was to do his job, get paid and then move on to pastures new when he'd had enough. He had already seen the Earl from a distance, a slim fellow with a dark beard, very different from Earl Spencer but just as impressive and well connected. He had been interviewed by the Head Gardener and that was enough for him. He knew that one only really saw the owner of the house on very special occasions or, when a big announcement had to be made to the staff such as the one given out last year back, at Althorp, by Lord Spencer when Queen Victoria died. When the old lady had passed away at Osborne House the 'Red Earl' himself had gathered everybody into the Drawing Room to announce the news.

Belton House.

He turned his attention back to the blackbird again. It was only yards away from him and pulling away at a worm that seemed unwilling to surrender.

"Oh you will have to be tougher than that my friend," laughed Charles. "Go on pull the blighter!"

His conversation with the blackbird came to a halt with the arrival of Henry and it flew off without its prey.

"Come on Charles old boy, that's enough for today. Are you trying to show me up!"

In fact Henry had been on the other side of the gardens, trimming hedges, all of which seemed to have a mind of their own at this time of year.

"All right, I am on my way – that little cove up there wants his grub!" He nodded in the direction of the blackbird that settled a little way away on a stone edifice and called across to it. "You get those pesky slugs as well, do you hear?"

He picked up his dibber and trays. "I'll just take these back to the greenhouse."

"OK, but get a move on, I'm hungry!" Henry laughed. "If we smile sweetly at Cook, she may give us some dinner in the kitchen."

Charles didn't mind where he ate, so long as he ate. The Bothy was a small out building which housed all the gardening staff and the kitchen maids would bring food to them, but it was easier for everybody if room was made around the big table in the main kitchen. It was just a question of timing and avoiding the household staff as much as possible.

He carefully closed the greenhouse door and joined Henry on the path that lead up to the back of the big house. Such a size the place was! It seemed wicked to have a place so big for just one couple with no children when so many people had nowhere to go. However, Charles was not the jealous sort and he was quite contented with his lot.

"Just as grand as Althorp isn't it?" said Henry as they walked along, "how the other half live eh? We could have some bike rides around here."

The one thing that neither boy left at home were their bikes. They had initially travelled to Grantham by train with their bikes in the Goods Van. Charles had owned his since he was fourteen and had quickly learned to take care of it and used it to go backwards and forwards to work. His father John had a penny-farthing and often could be seen riding sedately around the village on it. However, his son did not 'do sedately' and he preferred the more modern standard one with two wheels of the same size!

Now their bikes were housed in a corner of the stables, much to the discomfiture of the grooms and stable lads. They, above anyone else, could see their jobs disappearing with the advent of the motor car and the general use of the cycle.

"Oh times they are a changing!" said Mr. Martin who was in charge of the stables, but he tolerated the lads and their bikes just so long as they did not frighten the horses. As far as Charles was concerned he would be using it to ride home the next time he had some days off. It was a long way but better than spending his hard earned money on train fares.

The two boys continued striding up to the house and it wasn't long before they could smell the dinner and the faint aroma of boiled ham. They stopped at the outside sink which was filled with water from the well and washed the dirt from their hands before tentatively poking their heads round the door to the kitchen.

"Come on you two." It was the Assistant Cook looking very homely in her white apron and cap. "Sit yourselves down."

They sat down at the big table along with another young gardener called Fred and two grooms and were soon tucking into boiled ham and vegetables followed by suet pudding. Most of the other employees were married men and they had gone home to their families. The household staff had already had theirs and were back either doing their various duties or finishing for the day. Charles thought he was very honoured to be allowed to sit in the kitchen. Usually it was in the Bothy.

It was a very grand house but Charles saw very little of it beyond the huge kitchen which was the total domain of Mrs. Betty Carstairs, the Chief Cook. He knew, of course, that there was a great big marble ballroom and dozens of bedrooms and drawing rooms, some of which were set aside for visiting Royalty. However, he wasn't really interested in their lives. The main thing was that he had a job and was paid.

Just at the moment he was concentrating on his meal and failed to see the young scullery maid looking at him with a twinkle in her eye.

He was a good looking boy, slim with dark hair brushed to one side with a side parting. His skin, just like Henry's was brown and weathered. However, Henry was nearly twenty and much more interested in young ladies than he was.

The young girl, whose name turned out to be Alice, took away his plate.

"I'll bet you would like some steamed pudding now wouldn't you?" she twinkled.

"Oi, oi!" laughed Fred, "your luck is in Charles, she can charm anybody with a steamy pudding."

Charles took no notice and took what was offered whilst, at the same time, looking around the huge kitchen with its shelves covered in shiny copper pots. It was even larger than the one at Althorp. He thought of his mother's little kitchen and smiled to himself. "Henry's right, How the other half do live!"

Once fed, the three boys made their way back to the Bothy.

"You missed your chance there!" said Fred "I think that little scullery maid liked the cut of your jib."

Charles coloured up. "You can try as much as you like Fred," he grinned "but I am not ready for any of that yet. I like my freedom too much and I have seen my brother Joseph tied down. He can't go anywhere without his fiancé in his shadow."

"Well maybe he wants his fiancée to be in his shadow," laughed Henry. "You'll learn my lad, you will learn. Someone will come along and you will want her in your shadow all the time."

"Or maybe you in her shadow instead?" said Fred.

"Never!" retorted Charles. "I will never be in any woman's shadow."

"Ha ha, famous last words, old chap, famous last words."

"Hey look," whispered Henry, changing the conversation as they walked down the path, "look at those two pretty chambermaids. I like the one with the red hair."

"Trust you!" grunted Charles, "it's all you think about."

"Well don't you?" laughed Fred. "I fancy the other one!"

"Well off you go then," replied Charles. "I have to write a letter home anyway"

The girls looked in their direction and giggled.

"Come on Fred," cried Henry, "let's go and use our charms!"

"If I were you I would have a wash first!" giggled Charles. "Look at you, how can you expect a young lady to go out with you?"

It was true. Henry looked ruefully down at his filthy trousers and shoes. It was a wonder that Cook had allowed him in the kitchen.

"Well, I'll still give it a try!" said Fred. "Look, they are looking our way – we don't want to miss a chance."

Charles left them to it and carried on back to the Bothy. His letter was not going to write itself.

Five minutes later Fred and Henry appeared, looking flustered.

"Quick, we have got to change," panted Fred, "they have said we can take them for a walk so long as we get tidied up. They have gone back to their rooms to get their dresses on."

"With a bit of luck we'll get them off," laughed Henry as he flew down the room and rifled under his bed for his box containing his spare clothes and changed his breeches and shirt while his friend did the same. Charles just watched, faintly amused.

Clearly they had the Bothy to themselves just at the moment but there could be half a dozen young boys sharing it at any one time. They were kept in check by Albert Horrocks. He was a married man but his home was on the premises so it was no hardship to spend time keeping an eye on his young charges and making sure that they got clean sheets from the laundry and kept the place up to scratch.

Fred and Henry spent some time making themselves presentable and Charles was left in peace to carry on with his letter. The girls didn't really interest him. He was more interested in his bike and in the latest technologies. The world was changing fast. He had even read that it was possible to see pictures move at a place called a Picture House. Mr. Horrocks had mentioned that one of these establishments had opened in London. At the same time there was the Boer War going on in Africa. It was already an altogether different world to the one his father and mother had been brought up in. They had been born at the time of the Crimean War and Florence Nightingale.

"There are always damn wars," he thought to himself.

He also vaguely wondered if he would see the 3rd Earl or Lady Adelaide about the gardens the following day. He did sometimes but always in the distance because generally he worked round the back of the house. The Earl, despite the fact that he was now retired from the Army, still seemed to keep himself busy with all the patronages he had. He was also the Honorary Colonel of the 4th Battalion of the Lincolnshire Regiment and of the Lincolnshire Yeomanry, not to mention the 4th Battalion of the Hertfordshire Regiment.

"It's all very posh here, but not much different to Althorp," he wrote to his parents. "There are always lots of comings and goings by the gentry. Hope you are all keeping well and I will try and get home soon."

He finished his letter and then lay on his bed but his peace was soon shattered by the return of Henry and Fred, slightly the worse for drink and looking a little dishevelled, but with news that they would be seeing the girls again.

"We will fix you up with that Alice next time," said Henry, "you see if we don't."

◆ ◆ ◆

PITSFORD WAS NOT THE only place where the residents were awoken by the local cockerel. Charles was in a deep sleep when the Belton House cockerel decided that it was time for everyone to get up.

"Dang thing!" muttered Henry from underneath his sheets. "It can't be time to get up already."

However, Mrs. Horrocks had been in and already there was a kettle bubbling away on the range and a big saucepan of porridge for them to help themselves to. Life as a gardener in rural Lincolnshire was about to continue.

The boys had no sooner finished their porridge than the slamming of the Bothy door announced the arrival of Albert with their instructions and the news for the day. He was already dressed, ready for action, in his thick trousers and strong gumboots.

"Henry, I want you to go back up to the walled garden and attend to the roses, and Fred, you can go and help the rest of the gardeners in the outer fields. I notice that there is a lot of undergrowth that needs cutting back. You Charles, get back to the kitchen garden and I would suggest you speak to Cook about getting some salt to put on the tails of those slugs." He was a big portly man with greying hair and a big handlebar moustache. His face and arms were brown and weathered with the years of working outside.

"I've not finished yet!" he cried, as the boys got up to leave "Her ladyship is organising a Ball next Saturday so I want extra hard work from you all. I'm getting extra staff to do down by the Italian garden and the Orangery."

Although the main gardening staff, including the married ones, numbered no more than about twenty, this amount was greatly increased at the time of special events.

Everyone put on their black gardening aprons with the big pockets and then dispersed to do their respective jobs while Charles made his way to the kitchen to see if he could get some salt. His apron was huge and nearly reached the ground. He tied the string round his waist and brushed it down to make sure he was a bit decent to go in the kitchen. Although muscular for his age, he was quite slim. He measured about five foot nine inches tall and had a mop of dark brown hair parted on the side. His eyes were grey/green and, as a child, they had been capable of melting his mother when he was naughty and needed scolding. He had attempted to grow a moustache like Henry and Fred, and which was the fashion of the day, but wasn't quite as successful as they were.

He was met by Daisy, one of the young Parlour maids who had gone out the night before with Henry and Fred. She was the one with the red hair that Henry had been quite taken with. Clearly she had been taken with him too because the first question she asked was "where is Henry working today?"

Charles laughed. "Oh he is way over on the other side of the gardens but I will tell him you asked about him if you like. He is all set to walk out with you again – at least, he is hoping!"

She coloured up to the roots of her hair and stuttered.

"Oh yes, well maybe" she said "I don't want to appear forward though. Come, I will get you the salt."

He followed her into the kitchen which, by now, was a hive of industry with scullery maids and footmen and kitchen maids all falling over each other to get their jobs done. In the centre of all the activity, at the big wooden table, the Kitchen Maid was rolling pastry under the watchful eye of Cook.

"This is all very well!" she said "that man Horrocks should get his own supply of salt instead of pinching ours." Nevertheless, she found a chunk and hammered it with the rolling pin to break it up.

"Thank you" said Charles as Daisy put it into a big jar. "I'll put that on their tails."

He did feel that it wasn't a very nice way to get rid of slugs but it did the trick on the few rows of lettuce that were in the Kitchen Garden.

He spent the day tidying up the lettuce and also the new peas that were starting to poke through, and the weeding, there was always weeding.

If, however, he thought he was going to rest from his labours with another evening on his own writing letters then he was badly mistaken. Henry and Fred had other ideas and shattered any illusions he might have had when they all gathered for their meal.

"I think Daisy and Phyllis are going to bring Alice with them tonight" said Fred as he and Charles washed up the dishes. Henry was already by the big sink in the corner of the Bothy trimming his moustache which he was quite proud of.

"Oh thank you for telling me!" grunted Charles. "I don't want to go out with the poor girl!"

"Now you can't let a lady down," called Henry. "That would be very bad form."

Reluctantly Charles got himself ready. He went outside to the outhouse where they kept the tin bath and cleaned himself up. He hadn't been shaving long but, even so, everybody thought he was older than what he was, probably including Alice.

"There is a Fair on down on the village green and if we get a move on we can take the girls and get them back before everywhere is locked up for the night," said Henry as he struggled into his starched collar.

It wasn't long before the three boys were calling at the back door that lead down to the kitchens 'below stairs' and were ready to meet the three giggling girls. Charles was less than impressed but he quite fancied the idea of the fair and going on the roundabouts and trying his hand at the coconut shy and it was a lovely sunny evening.

Henry, ever the gallant gentleman, took Daisy's arm and lead the way across the grass and out through the side gate. Already they could hear the sounds of the barrel organ and the cries and squeals of people on the swings and roundabouts and soon they were all joining in with the melee. There was only one problem as far as Charles was concerned. This 'Alice woman' could not stop talking! She was a pretty girl with long blonde hair coiled up in a big bun at the back of her head and a trim pert little figure, but the minute she opened her mouth she put him off! She had a broad Irish accent which he could barely understand and she did not stop for breath. By the time they arrived at the Fair he knew where she came from, which was Belfast, and every intimate detail about every member of her very large extended family.

"Come on" he called, hoping to shut her up. "Let's go on the prancing horses!" It didn't stop her though.

"Oooh look Charles, look at that man over there trying to pick up those weights, oh and look at the juggler over there, and look....." and so it went on until Charles decided that the best plan was to let her chatter and just say "yes" at various intervals.

For all that the evening passed quickly and it didn't seem five minutes before they had to get the bus back.

"We had better get a shift on" said Daisy "or the Butler will be locking us out.

Charles had met the Butler one or two times. He was the most important person of the household as far as the 'downstairs' staff were concerned, although Cook would have disagreed with that. His name was Mr. Watkins and he was quite an imposing, tall man, with a handlebar moustache.

Fortunately the bus was on time and they watched as the horses pulled it along the street towards them.

"Bless them, they look so tired," said Phyllis.

"You are riding in a thing of the past" replied Fred, "most of these are being replaced by horseless buses these days."

There was much screaming and giggling from the ladies as they all sat on the top deck but the horses didn't seem to mind.

"Sssh!" hissed Henry as they all piled out and walked down the drive. "We don't want to disturb his Lordship."

Soon they paired off and Fred and Henry disappeared into a darkened corner just outside the kitchens with their conquests. Charles had no desire to get to know Alice any better and so, with a hasty kiss on the cheek he thanked her for her company and left her at the door. If she had been hoping for him to arrange another date she was to be disappointed. She looked much deflated and for once she seemed to be lost for words.

"Thank you Charles" she said "maybe I shall see you tomorrow?"

"*Not if I see you first!*" he said under his breath as she closed the kitchen door.

"Blow that!" he said to himself. "Anybody that ends up with her would be better off deaf."

Despite all the efforts of Henry and Fred when they arrived back, no amount of persuasion would ever induce him to walk out with that young lady again. He would wait until he was ninety for the right woman if he had to and Alice O'Brien definitely was not the one.

◆ ◆ ◆

THE GRAND BALL WAS a sumptuous affair and extra staff was taken on to help with the catering. It was mostly attended by old soldiers and dignitaries from the many organisations that

The Earl associated with. Of course, the gardening staff were not allowed round the front as the carriages arrived so they couldn't see much, but they could certainly hear it, the cackle of voices and the music coming from the large ballroom. In the kitchen everyone from Cook downwards were run off their feet chasing backwards and forwards to make sure everything was all right.

"Aw, they are welcome to it!" said Charles. Henry had been poking around the grounds to try and see if he could find a way to get round the front without being seen, but it was a light night and he didn't want to take the chance. Occasionally they caught sight of a couple walking arm in arm, the gentleman in full Army uniform and the lady in a long flowing gown, but only because the gentry had strolled out for some fresh air.

"I am a man of simple tastes" went on Charles. "They used to have grand events where Henry and I last worked, put on by the Earl Spencer, but I would just as soon go and listen to the Salvation Army Band in the village.

Henry and Fred gave him a quizzical look.

"Don't worry Fred" joked Henry "he will grow up soon. He is only seventeen."

Life as a gardener at Belton House in the heart of Lincolnshire went on.

◆ ◆ ◆

TALK OF HOME MADE Charles feel a little guilty. He had been gone five months now and it was time he went home before the summer gave way to autumn. He had his bike and was used to riding all over the place. He would ride the forty miles or so home the next time he was due a few days off. If he started out early enough he would have a bit of time and then ride back a couple of days later. He was looking forward to seeing his brothers and sisters again and he would enjoy bicycling as long as the weather was with him. He wrote home and told his mother his plans. He would leave Henry and Fred to chase the girls. It wasn't that he didn't like girls. He did, but he just hadn't come across one that he had 'taken to' yet. Or, more importantly, in his view, that had taken to him. As for 'chatty' Alice, well he just couldn't cope with anyone who talked so much. In any case, since his lack of enthusiasm for her when they went to the Fair she had turned her attentions towards one of the footmen.

"Don't worry Charles my lad!" Albert Horrocks told him when his friends pulled his leg. "Don't you take any notice of these reprobates. There is plenty of time for you. You will get shackled down by a woman soon enough."

He actually had days off owing to him so he was able to go home for four days in early September when the weather was at its best. He was up with the lark and made sure his bicycle was in good working order. Then, following the road signs, and the direction of the sun, he set off on his journey back to Pitsford. Albert had very kindly spoken to his wife and she gave him a pile of bread and cheese for the journey.

"There you are my boy. You get on your way, but don't you be late back now" said Albert. It was Friday morning and he would not be due back until Monday night. He pushed the food into the bag he carried on his back. "Thank you Mr. Horrocks, don't worry, I won't be late. My mother will see to that."

With that he waved goodbye and set off on his journey.

It was a pleasant ride through the country lanes and he managed to have a couple of stops on the way to eat and to go behind a bush to relieve himself. There was very little on the roads other than a few horse and carts and carriages, and just occasionally a horseless carriage, spluttering along and spitting out exhaust fumes. These would rattle by and frighten the horses that were pulling the carts. Charles thought they were a bloomin' nuisance although he had to accept that they were probably here to stay and he knew that the towns were seeing more and more of them. One came passed him with the couple sat up high in the seats, the lady with her hat tied on with a scarf and the gentleman concentrating on his driving, but it wasn't long before Charles was overtaking them on his bike! *"They will have to do better than this if they are to catch on"* he thought, and decided that he would stick to two wheels!

After, what seemed like an eternity, he saw the signposts to Pitsford and he was riding down the familiar streets where he saw the faces of people he recognised. Then he turned the corner and there was his mother sitting in her usual place, outside the front door in the sunshine, doing her lace making. The minute she saw him she dropped everything and ran towards him as if he had been away for years instead of a few months.

He propped his bicycle against the wall and gave her an enormous hug as other members of the family emerged from the house. There was Emily and Rose and little Mabel, and not far behind them, his father. He wished that Rose looked a little better. She was a pretty girl, tall and dark haired like himself but she was so pale all the time and always seemed to be coughing. The rest of the family made up for her though. All were as brown as berries after the long hot summer they had just been through. He gave them all a hug and was happy to be taken through to the kitchen and hear about all they had been doing though he was also happy to stand up for a while! It had been a long ride and his backside was aching.

"I'll have to go into Northampton and see Joseph while I am here" he said "is he still busy baking his bread?"

"Yes, he bakes lovely bread" piped up Mabel "here I will get you some Charles." The six year old made her way to the larder while Elizabeth put the kettle on the kitchen range for some tea. Elizabeth went over to the cupboard and took out the accordion from where she had last put it away.

"Come on Charles, give us a quick tune," she said "we have missed this."

He took it from her and played a succession of Salvation Army songs and 'Down at the old Bull and Bush'.

"Well, there's a contrast" laughed Rose when he had finished. It all ended in giggling.

Later that day John would be home from the gardens where he worked and they could catch up on all the gossip and exchange gardening tips. He looked around the little kitchen. The whole house would fit inside the kitchen at Belton House and have room to spare. "I wouldn't swap it though" he thought "not for a gold clock."

With his backside totally rested he was happy to sit and listen to all the girls chattering.

After a while he wandered out into the back garden where his father's old penny-farthing bike was propped under an awning against the wall. He didn't really fancy riding back to Grantham on something like that, but John seemed to manage. There were also a couple of beehives along the side wall and a large fenced off area for the chickens. His family did try to be self-sufficient wherever they could. They really did stick to the family motto of 'if you couldn't grow it or make it then it wasn't worth having'.

The time passed all too quickly especially as he was enjoying being molly-coddled by his mother. He could cope with more of that but he wanted to be self-sufficient too and he had a living to make back at Grantham. He knew he wouldn't be stopping there for ever but he wanted to make a good impression while he could.

The following day he cycled into Northampton and looked up his brother. Joseph was staying in digs with a family by the name of Walker but today he was in the shop selling the bread.

"Two small loaves please!" laughed Charles as he arrived at the counter. Joseph looked up and was delighted to see his brother.

"Why look at you!" he said "I swear you have grown another inch in the past few months. Come on round this side of the counter and tell me all that you have been doing. A young lady appeared from the back of the shop her hands covered in flour.

"This is Emmie" said Joseph. "We are engaged now."

Charles took to her immediately and gave her a gallant kiss on the cheek.

"Actually" she said, "my name is Frances Emma but they call me Emmie."

"He needs a good woman Emmie" said the younger man, "he needs someone to keep an eye on him and keep him out of mischief."

He dodged the piece of dough that his brother threw at him and it landed in the corner of the shop seconds before a customer arrived to buy some bread.

"Don't know why you had to go further up north though" said Joseph later when they were having tea and cakes. "If it were me I would be venturing south – that seems to be where all the action is. Just think, if you were down south you might see King Edward's Coronation procession when it happens."

Charles, like all his family, was a staunch royalist but he was quite happy with seeing the pictures in the newspapers.

"It's all right Joe" he replied "I'll soldier on where I am. I like it because I am in the kitchen garden and I enjoy seeing all the vegetables grow."

"Except for the pesky slugs eh Charles?"

"Ha ha, yes Joe, except for the pesky slugs."

Nevertheless Joseph's words did get Charles thinking. Maybe he had been a bit hasty. After all his Grandpa and Grandma Howard were a bit further down south and he could have been nearer to them if he had thought about it.

"Oh well, I have cooked my goose now" he thought as he bid Joseph and Emmie goodbye. He was only young and time was on his side.

◆ ◆ ◆

CHARLES SPENT THE REST of his few days off in catching up with old friends from school and visiting his Grandma Alice. He looked at her hands reddened with constant laundry work and noticed how she had to struggle to see everything she was doing in the little tiny cottage that had been her home since the children had all left. Now she was on her own but it didn't seem to get her down. She was always cheery but he couldn't help hoping that his mother would not end up like that. He sat with her for a while and then bid her goodbye. This time he had a train to catch. His bike would go in the Guards Van as before. It was all very well cycling all that distance home but he could not take the chance of something going wrong and being late back.

Elizabeth and his sisters came and waved him off at the station. He gave them all a hug. He knew he didn't want to stay at Belton House for ever, but just for now it would do.

"Remember my son" his mother said as she hugged him again. "You look after your pennies and the pennies will look after your pounds."

"Look after yourself brother" said Rosa.

"You look after yourself Rose" smiled Charles as he hugged her again. "I want to see that cough better next time I come home and more roses in your cheeks."

"All aboard whose going aboard!" The station master shouted his warning and everybody scrambled on to the train and leaned out of the windows. Within seconds it was chugging loudly out of the little station and kicking up so much smoke that the onlookers were soon out of sight.

Life at Belton Hall, with his friends Henry and Fred, would go on – for the time being at least but it was the last time that he would see Rose.

CHAPTER III

Easthampstead Park, 1901

Alice Jones looked in the mirror, took a deep breath and made sure that her starched white cap was straight on her thick black hair. She had been in her new job working for the 6th Earl of Downshire for a few weeks now and was still getting used to her new surroundings. He was also the Earl of Hillsborough so he was very grand indeed, although she had got very used to mixing with the gentry so she ought not to be nervous any more. After all, she had just come from a very prestigious job working as Parlour Maid for Lord Norman-ton at his enormous and palatial home, Somerley, near Ringwood in Hampshire. It had been a good job but she never knew where she would be next! One minute the family would up sticks and move to The Earl's home in London, which suited her down to the ground as she came from nearby Barnes, so she could get home very easily, but then, hardly with any warning the whole household would have to move back down to Ringwood whenever the mood took him or his wife Caroline.

She thought back to her time there. Nobody could say it wasn't interesting and it certainly was a beautiful establishment to work in. Lord Normanton numbered many famous people among his guests including the Marquess of Queensbury and his son Lord Alfred Douglas who was the companion of Oscar Wilde.

"Now Lord Alfred was interesting!" thought Alice as she smiled at her reflection in the mirror and brushed down her apron.

She recalled what some of the servants below stairs used to say about his relationship with the famous Irish author and playwright!. In fact the servants still had plenty to say even here at Easthampstead. They even said that Alfred was Oscar's boyfriend of all things! It hadn't seemed possible to her so it came as a complete surprise when one of the grooms showed her the newspaper relating to all the scandal. She knew Oscar Wilde had gone to jail of course, but despite all the gossip it largely went over her head as she was only sixteen back then and didn't understand what the older servants were talking about. Also, her parents hid the newspapers out of the way whenever she and her younger brothers and sisters were at home. She remembered her father, Joshua, saying "this is not suitable reading for young ladies" and then taking the paper away and hiding it..

"Oh well, it takes all sorts!" she thought to herself, but it certainly went against anything she had ever been taught, especially by her father who was a man of the Church and a Lay Reader.

She had been in the employment of Lord Normanton at Somerley since she was fifteen so when she became twenty-two, she thought it was time to move on. She had done well, moving up from Kitchen Maid to Parlour Maid but she felt there was more to life than this and she had yet to meet a nice beau that took her fancy. Maybe a change would open up new horizons in that direction too! She therefore felt it was 'divine providence' when she saw the position of Lady's Maid offered in the Newspaper., It was a step up and the Agency that had advertised the job were happy with being able to send someone with her experience to work in the Earl of Hillsborough's household. Not that she expected to see much of him. He, like her previous employer, spent much of his time at The House of Lords in

London or, of course, in his case, at his palatial residence, Hillsborough Castle, in County Down, Northern Ireland.

"You never know Mother", she said excitedly "when she told her about the new job, "I may get to accompany him to Ireland. That will be an adventure."

She checked herself in the mirror again and made sure her apron was spic and span and that her shoes were shiny. She was of slight build, almost petite some people called her five foot two inch slim figure. Her crowning glory was her black shiny hair which she always washed with rain water, and she had dark brown eyes that had turned many young men's heads, but none that Alice had taken to.

"One of these days I will meet someone who will take my fancy" she thought "maybe I am too particular for my own good!"

Easthampstead Park on the outskirts of Bracknell, stood in 5,000 acres of land and was the 'centre of the Universe' as far as the gentry were concerned, especially during Ascot week and Alice already knew that it would be a place where there would be many parties and balls to prepare for. It was very grand and even boasted its own private menagerie of monkeys and a brown bear which were kept in cages in the Orangery. Alice did not like that one bit but she supposed that Lord and Lady Downshire could do whatever they wanted to do.

It was early days yet following the death of Queen Victoria and, just like everywhere else, portraits of Her Majesty were still shrouded in black and people wondered what things would be like once King Edward had been crowned.

"I don't think he will live that long" her father had said "look at the weight he carries and he is a sick man even now." It was hard to disagree.

Finally, satisfied that she looked decent enough, she made her way to the Drawing Room. It was an enormous room and required a great amount of dusting but one of the Parlour Maids would do most of that. Indeed, young Betty was already there getting busy with a dustpan and brush.

"You beat me to it today Betty!" laughed Alice. She looked around at the dust which showed up in the light from the sun beaming in through the window. "I think we have a job on our hands today." Alice's job mostly involved looking after her ladyship, but she was happy to help out in the Drawing Room or anywhere else that was needed.

Betty was three years her junior, a plump young girl with dark hair and who came from Bethnal Green. A true cockney.

"Cor blimey Alice, I know" she replied "My young man James said that someone has invented a dust sucking machine. I think we could do with one of those."

Alice wasn't sure if this was true or not but she certainly wouldn't say no to a dust sucking machine. In the meantime, though, it had to be the dustpan and brush. It would keep them occupied for the entire morning.

The one thing that was not occupied was her brain and so she found her mind wandering back to the last time she was home. She'd had a month between her jobs so she had plenty of time to catch up with her friends and family. She thought fondly of her parents, Sarah and Joshua Kirck. Sarah was an Essex girl through and through and came from a family of publicans. Joshua, on the other hand, came from Richmond and was a carpenter and a lay reader in Church. They could not be more opposite if they tried but it seemed to work, so much so that Alice had four sisters and two brothers, very few of whom had been home when she had been there as most, like her, were in service.

Of course, her youngest brother Frederick Charles, was totally spoilt by all the family. Alice could see why though. Joshua Junior was the oldest and married now and he had a very good job as an architect. She felt a burst of pride when she thought of him. But then her parents had girl after girl. All were loved but she could well remember the cry of "not another girl" as Annie, Edith, Emily and Elizabeth were born. Now they had young Frederick – or Charlie – as the family called him. He was still at school but going to the very smart Latymer College to learn languages.

At various times while she was at home her sisters had called in to see her and make a fuss of Charlie.

"See how clever he is" remarked Emily one day when she came home on a day off "learning French and German."

"But really, what use is it?" whispered young Elizabeth under her breath "that's not building anything you can sell."

Alice couldn't help but agree but her mother overheard them whispering.

"I think your father knows what he is doing," she said. "Languages will be needed before long as people travel more. They will want clever boys like Charlie to translate. Even now, our politicians travel abroad and they will pay well to have someone who speaks the lingo."

"Well, I think he would have been better learning to be an architect like our brother Joshua," retorted Elizabeth.

Little did any of them know that in fourteen years time all would be bitterly regretting that Charlie ever learned languages!

Alice carried on with her dusting and thought of Edith and Emily. They also were in service working for none other than Frederick Temple, the Archbishop of Canterbury. She felt a slight pang of disappointment that she had not seen her older brother Joshua while she was at home but he had been on The Channel Islands where he was working on some designs for a row of houses that were to be built there.

"Yes, they are all fleeing the nest one by one" she thought, "Mother won't know where she is soon."

Her thoughts were interrupted be the sound of the bell on the wall.

"Looks like her ladyship is ready for you," said Betty. "Come on, penny for them!"

"Oh I was just thinking of them all at home," she laughed "and wondering if they are coping without me." She threw down her duster and plumped up a few cushions. "I'd better go. Can you iron the papers Betty and then get to the kitchen to see if they want you in there."

She brushed down her apron and straightened her cap again and then walked up the large staircase to the main bedroom. Lady Katherine was there half dressed and just waiting for Alice to button her up at the back. Clearly she had already had her bath which had been prepared by one of the Chambermaids.

"Good morning Alice"

"Good morning Ma'am" replied Alice. "Nice one today eh!"

She was a nice woman. Alice liked her but the Marquess was away a lot and most of the servants suspected that she might have a number of admirers. Who could blame her for accepting their favours if she was deserted so much. Of course, some of the time, both she and the rest of the household would go to Lord Downshire's residence of Hillsborough in Northern Ireland, but just lately she had remained at Easthampstead and busied herself organising parties. She was married to one of the richest men in England. Her husband's full name was Arthur Wills John Wellington Trumbell Hill but, much to everyone's amusement he just called himself plain old Arthur Hill. He owned 5,000 acres here at Easthampstead and another 115,000 acres in Northern Ireland.

"Ah well" thought Alice to herself "money doesn't always bring happiness."

She had seen his lordship a few times. He was quite tall and lean looking and with a handlebar moustache. When he was at home he seemed to like nothing better than going round the estate in a farmer's smock and helping the gardening and farming staff. He owned a horseless carriage and had recently employed a chauffeur but would often push him out of the way so that he could take a turn or he would drive a fire engine around the estate. He seemed to be so different from his refined wife and very different from Lord Normanton.

"Opposites - a bit like my parents" thought Alice to herself with a grin, "but with money."

"What are you smiling about Alice?" said Katherine as she caught sight of her in the mirror.

"Oh nothing Madam, you really don't want to know!" she replied.

She was a beautiful woman with thick brown hair and she sat quietly while Alice pinned it up for her. Then once she was convinced that her employer was properly dressed for the day she took her leave.

"I'll get some breakfast sent to the Dining Room for you Ma'am" she said as she left her employer to her own devices. Later she would be back to check that the chambermaid had been in and tidied the bedroom properly. Now it was time to go and get something to eat for herself. She had already had a bit of breakfast but that seemed like ages ago.

◆ ◆ ◆

ALICE HAD BEEN AT Easthampstead Park six months and autumn was turning to winter when the normal routine of the household was tragically interrupted. It had been her afternoon off and she spent it writing letters in the room she shared with Betty. She was just about to go to the kitchen to see if Cook had anything nice for tea when the door crashed open almost knocking her down. It was Mary the Kitchen Maid, a young girl of just sixteen years of age.

"Alice, Alice" she cried as tears rolled down her face. She was in hysterics. "You can't believe what has happened." She threw herself down on the bed in floods of tears and then jumped up again and grabbed Alice by the arm. "Come, come, it's Jenny – there has been a terrible, terrible accident! It is just too awful!"

The two girls ran along the downstairs corridor although Alice still didn't really know what had happened. It was obviously something very serious because there were sounds of kitchen staff running in all directions and bells ringing wildly.

"She is in the Scullery!" shouted Peter, who was one of the valets.

"For goodness sake Mary!" puffed Alice, "what on earth has happened?" All her attempts at making herself look smart were going out of the window in their efforts to rush and she could already feel the pins slipping in her hair. Then she heard it. Loud, very loud screaming, like a pig in torture.

"Jenny fell into the tub of boiling water in the scullery!" puffed Mary.

"What!" Alice was horrified.

They reached the scullery, only to be pushed to one side by Cook. They had now been joined by the lady of the house, Katherine and some of her friends, closely followed by James Chapman the Butler.

"Oh my God, my God!" she cried as she took charge of the situation. She turned to the Butler. "James, James, run, or get a bicycle and get the doctor immediately!" The screams of the girl were pervading the whole house. Then suddenly they stopped. Alice, Betty and Mary, along with other downstairs staff watched, as the men tried to carry the poor girl into the main kitchen without touching the scalded area, which wasn't easy as her whole body was now covered in red blisters. She was dead before the doctor arrived with an ambulance. Alice couldn't help but feel that they would have been better off leaving her on the floor of the scullery instead of carting her around, but she didn't dare say anything. After all, she hadn't been a member of the household for long!

The whole house was in an absolute uproar. In the corner of the Scullery two of the laundry boys were huddled on the floor shaking and trying not to scream out as one of the older household members tried to calm them down. Apparently it had been them that had pulled her out. Both had scalded hands and arms and were in terrible pain. Somebody had the forethought to get a big bowl of cold water and already Cook was plunging their arms in it and then wrapping them up in cloth. She learned later from the doctor that it was the best thing she could have done. For all that, neither young man would be fit for work for weeks.

News of the terrible accident reached Lord Downshire who had been over on the other side of the estate and he came rushing back in time to see the poor girl carried away.

"You lads, get in my car. I shall take you to the hospital myself, and don't you worry, I will keep your job here for you for as long as it takes for you to recover."

With that they were off down the drive in a cloud of dust and lots of steam from the engine.

Young Jenny was buried on the Estate and Lord and Lady Downshire plus the whole of the staff attended her funeral and tried to comfort her distraught parents. Like Mary, she was just sixteen.

"I still don't really know how she did it" said Alice to Ethel Groves, who was also a Scullery Maid.

"Easily done" replied Ethel, "there was a stool by the big tub and we all think she stood on that to lean right over to get something out which was beyond her reach. The water was boiling and the stool slipped from under her. That was that!"

"Just terrible," muttered Alice.

"Well, it is not something I am going to do, I can tell you that," said Ethel. "If any laundry goes out of my reach I shall use the tongs or it will get left until the water has cooled down."

Despite the terrible accident, Alice settled down to her duties as Lady's Maid, making sure that Katherine had everything she needed and helping out in the Drawing Room including ensuring that the newspapers were ironed every morning. She felt she would never get Jenny's screams from out of her head though and it was the topic of conversation 'downstairs' for a very long time.

Once everyone thought it was 'decent' after the death of Queen Victoria the parties started again. She did vaguely wonder if she would meet a nice young man to walk out with but nobody really took her fancy despite the advances of the grooms and the valets. She was twenty-two now and already her older brother Joshua and younger sister Emily had beaten her to it. At least though she was a bit further north now, and slightly nearer to London, so that she could get home more easily. It was a bit of a trek from her last position at Ringwood. Now it wasn't so far from nearby Bracknell into London when she had a day or two off. Also nobody could ever say that life at Easthampstead Park was dull.

◆ ◆ ◆

THE CORONATION OF EDWARD VII and Alexandra took place on 9th August 1902 and they took on extra staff at the Estate to cope with the visitors.

"About time" said Cook as she supervised the Kitchen Maids making puddings, "the poor Queen has been dead eighteen months."

Alice had finished her duties and had joined the staff to one side of the kitchen for a cup of tea. She hadn't seen much of her Ladyship lately as she always seemed to be out and chose not to have her maid with her.

"The King had a big operation on a stomach abscess" said Luke who was a new valet and seemed to know everything.

"Yuk, don't talk about stomach abscesses in my kitchen," said Cook. "Come on, off with you, jobs to do, jobs to do."

In fact the Coronation procession had been altered because of the delay and a second parade that should have been held the following day had to be cancelled because of the Kings health. He did however manage to attend the Review of the Fleet at Spithead and met with three Commanders from the Boer War which had only just finished earlier that year.

There always seemed to be something to gossip about at Easthampstead and if it wasn't the antics of his Lordship then it was the continued mutterings about her Ladyship. Alice kept quiet through it all but she, above anybody else, knew that all was not well between her employers. She got on well with Lady Katherine but realised that there was more to her than met the eye.

All was confirmed when Ethel came rushing into the kitchen the following day carrying a copy of The Tatler.

"Hey look at this" she cried "Lord and Lady Downshire are divorcing!"

Alice wasn't surprised but she gathered around with the others and read the article. Lord Downshire was suing his wife for divorce.

"Oh dear, I wonder where that will leave us?" said Luke. "Trust the gentry to make us the last to know."

They had been joined by James Chapman.

"I don't think it will make much difference at all" he replied "anyway, it is not for us to gossip." Nevertheless, he took the magazine and read the article carefully.

"It will affect you Alice" said Cook totally ignoring the Butler, "I expect Lady Katherine will have to leave."

Alice left and went to her room feeling a little subdued and unsettled.

Miss Alice Jones.

CHAPTER IV

Big Changes, 1906

Charles sat on a wooden bench near to the Orangery at Belton and surveyed his latest efforts at topiary. He had learned so much from Albert Horrocks in the past five years. He was almost like a second father to him. He had trimmed it into the shape of a bird and now it was just a question of cleaning up the fallen leaves and getting on with some dead heading of the roses. He had enjoyed his job here at Belton House but it was really time to move on. He was twenty-two now and if he was to ever become a husband and a father he would have to get a job that paid more money. Not that he had anybody on the horizon at the moment. There had been a few dalliances which had come to nothing and, thank goodness, that chatter-box Alice from the kitchen had left him alone once she found he wasn't interested. She had set her sights on one of the grooms.

"Hello Charles! You've done a good job there old boy!" It was his friend Henry pushing along a wheelbarrow that was full of stinking manure.

"Whew Henry, take that away!" laughed Charles. "What a stink!"

"Just got it from the stables" replied Henry. "I'm just taking it to dump by the roses. This will put goodness in the soil."

He trundled off taking his stink with him – or at least most of it. It still lingered.

"Your new wife won't fancy you with that perfume!" laughed Charles.

"Ah, she's getting used to it by now" his friend shouted back.

He would miss Henry if he moved on, but the friend that had come with him from Althorp House was married now. He married Daisy, the kitchen maid just last year and all of the staff had attended the wedding which was a really happy affair and lifted Charles out of the doldrums that he had been in for some time.

The talk of the roses and the knowledge that he would soon be going round dead-heading, and pruning in some cases, made him suddenly think of his sister Rose and his eyes filled with tears. She had passed away three years ago at the ridiculously young age of sixteen.

"Oh drat!" he cursed out loud as he thought of it again, "she had her whole life in front of her." He thought back to that day when he had first found out that she was so ill.

"Oh drat!" he said again out loud and slung his pruning shears down on the ground with force. The last three years had gone by so quickly and it was hard to think that she would have been nineteen now. It seemed like only five minutes ago since he had first arrived here with Henry. Now he could actually grow a proper moustache and his friend was married.. He remembered back to the day when he got the letter from his mother about his sister.

It had been winter time and he had been in the greenhouse cleaning up the old pots and trays when Albert Horrocks came in carrying a letter for him that had been given to him by the Butler to pass on to Charles. The words TB sprang out at him from the letter straight away and he sunk down to his knees on the floor.

"What's up old chap" said Albert. "You look like you have seen a ghost."

"It's my sister Rose Mr. Horrocks. She has TB and is gravely ill."

"Then go home my boy. There is little to do here with the winter approaching. You take a few days off and go home to your family."

Charles did not need to be told twice. He gathered up his bag and said goodbye to Henry and Fred and then rushed to get his bike. It was a long way in the cold but the exercise would keep him warm. It was just as easy to cycle, in his opinion, than to go on a train that could be very unreliable at this time of year – and cold. Besides, there had very recently been a train accident at Grantham where a sleeper train had left the rails. Fourteen had been killed and there were still train delays as a result. He didn't want to chance that.

Rose had passed away even while his mother's letter was in the post but he was just in time for the funeral. Everyone was distraught but TB was so common.

"So many have had it in the village" said a tearful Elizabeth and I am afraid my Rosa did not escape it." Everyone called her Rose but she would always be Rosa to her mother. Charles's father John stood with his back to the kitchen range and just grunted. If he spoke he would cry and he didn't want to do that in front of the family. Somebody had to keep a stiff upper lip.

Charles went with his mother to see her lying in the mortuary. She looked so peaceful. He stared at her lying there for a while and then slowly walked back to his mother and put his arm around her.

"My lovely young Rosa is in heaven now son" said Elizabeth. It would be her unswerving faith that would keep her going.

The one thing about a funeral is that it did bring the whole family together and his grandparents from Thornborough attended, as did his grandma Alice of course, and Joe, and Joseph with his new wife Emmie. It was nice to see them all but not under those circumstances.

A few spots of rain forced his mind back to the present day at Belton House and he got up and walked across the beautifully kept lawns in front of the Orangery. He went across to the rose gardens and tried to put the sadness of the passing of young Rosa out of his mind. It was a long time ago now but he doubted if he would ever get used to it. She was too young.

Despite the threatened rain, the sun was shining and if she was up there, looking down, then she would expect him to do a good job. Many of the roses had been battered in recent rains but he dead headed those that were beyond repair and allowed the existing blooms to do their stuff almost as though he were doing it in his sister's name. He bent down and smelt one and it was infinitely better than Henry's manure which he had dumped further up the garden. Well, that would keep him busy for a while digging that lot in!

Since the death of Rose he had mostly travelled back and forth on the train on his visits home. In fact, he had been so upset after coming back from the funeral that he had thrown his cycle into a corner of the yard and vowed he would never ride it again. He was convinced that if he had been on the train he might have got there quicker.

However, the next time he went home he found that his father had spent time in cleaning and looking after it and it was waiting for him in the shed. He didn't have the heart not to use it again. He didn't have his bicycle with him now though, because the next time he went home he would not be coming back! He would be finishing here at Belton House for ever. The Agency had offered him a position at a place called Aldermaston Court and he decided to take it. It seemed that after eight years of gardening between Althorp and Belton he had done his 'apprenticeship' and he could move south to a job with higher pay. Besides, the death of Rose had unsettled him and he needed a change and a new start.

"We shall be so sorry to lose you my lad," said Albert Horrocks when Charles told him of the planned move.

"I'll be sorry to go" replied Charles "but needs must. I just have this feeling that I want to go south, and this looks like a good position I am being offered. I need the change."

"Well, if ever you want to come back you are very welcome" muttered Albert.

Henry was beside himself but he also understood, though slightly jealous. He had a wife now and his home, for the time being, was here at Grantham, although he still had an urge to travel.

"You had better write though old chap," he said "no excuses now. You are a good writer, I know you are."

"Of course I will write" muttered Charles gruffly. He was sad at saying farewell to his friend.

They were also beside themselves in the kitchens and below stairs. They had all got used to

him being about and Cook was in floods of tears when he had his last meal in the kitchen.

"I'll bet they don't make a fuss of you at this place Aldermaston 'what ever it is' as I do" she said. She was an ample woman with an enormous bust and gave Charles a hug that he thought he would be smothered by. So distraught was everybody that he felt guilty leaving, especially as there were still roses to prune.

"*But still*" he thought, "*my replacement can carry on where I left off.*" He had an adventure about to begin and it was time to move on from the death of Rose and make a life for himself and maybe a future wife. Who knew what was round the corner, or who?

◆ ◆ ◆

THE BIGGEST ADVENTURE SO far in Charles's life was the train journey south and a trip on the London Underground. He had never been on such a long train journey before, firstly from Northampton to Euston and then on this monstrosity of a contraption that went under the ground to Paddington. The Agency had given him the instructions but he couldn't help but think he might have done better on his bicycle and going straight south as the crow flies. However, it was nearly ninety miles from Pitsford and a bit far, even for him on a 1900's bike that had seen better days. He had never been to London before so he took the opportunity to have a look around at the big buildings and all the hustle and bustle in and around Euston Station. He was a 'country bumpkin' at heart though and none of it really appealed to him, although he would have liked to have been in London and seen the Coronation of Edward VII. People were still talking about that and there were dozens of pictures in the papers.

The journey took him all day and he was glad to get to his destination. He certainly had not thought much of travelling underground. "I felt like a bloody mole" he said to his brother when he next wrote to him.

ALDERMASTON COURT[1] 1906

CHARLES RATCLIFF HEARD A nearby church clock chime four as he entered the gates and walked towards the imposing building in the autumn sunshine. It had been a long journey and he was glad to get there, especially as he had done justice to the sandwiches his mother had packed for him. His bag was heavy and he would be glad to put it down. This time he also had his accordion, or squeezebox, but he was beginning to

---

[1] ALDERMASTON COURT WAS the home of Sir Charles Edward Keyser and was set in 2,500 acres of woodland in Berkshire. It was just twenty-two miles from Easthampstead Park where Alice Jones was the Parlour Maid.

wish he hadn't bothered. It just made the things more cumbersome. He had never bothered at Belton, but it did occur to him that if he were in a Bothy with a few others then they might like the entertainment and it would stand him in good stead with them.

As he walked down the drive he could see already that there would be much to do. Winter was approaching and bushes were past their best and needed cutting back and the chrysanthemums in the flower beds were really on their last legs. It was a house that was very different to anywhere he had worked before and he stared at the gothic looking building with its tall clock tower all in red brick. It seemed to consist of gables and chimneys. He knew from experience that the best person to look for would be the Head Gardener and started to make his way around towards the back of the house. He turned a corner and came face to face with a fat man wearing a dark grey suit and a watch and chain across his ample belly.

"Oi, where are you going young man?" He stopped Charles in his tracks. He didn't think he could possibly be the Head Gardener.

"I am the new assistant gardener" said Charles "can you tell me where I can find the Head Gardener please?"

"Round the back – I've just been speaking to him" the portly figure replied. Suddenly Charles had a horrible feeling that he had bumped into Charles Keyser himself. It turned out he was right.

"Welcome to Aldermaston my boy. I'm Charles Keyser,"

Charles was caught off guard for a minute. He had not expected to see the owner of the house wandering around the kitchen gardens in a suit! He had dark hair waxed across his head so that it looked as though it was painted on, a florid face that looked like it was used to a drink or three, and a small black moustache.

"Ha ha" laughed his new employer "get yourself off round the back – he's in the office, You can't miss him."

"Thank you sir" stuttered Charles and parted company as quickly as he could. Nevertheless he seemed as though he was a nice enough old boy and he probably wouldn't have much to do with him anyway.

He found the Head Gardener, a Mr. Robert Roache, exactly where Mr. Keyser said he would be. It was the end of the day and one or two of the young gardening boys were getting ready to go to their homes whilst a couple of others, who presumably didn't live nearby were settling down in the Bothy for the evening.

"Come into my office young man" said Mr. Roache "and we will get to know each other."

It didn't take Charles long to realise that he liked his boss, which was just as well as he was already feeling a little 'home-sick' for Belton House. He had got used to the place.

"I just bumped into Mr. Keyser" he said as he put his bags down on the floor, "I nearly bowled him over when I came round the corner."

"Oh he is a funny old cove" Robert Roache laughed "got his finger into all sorts of pies but he is OK and we have some good old knees ups with the staff from some of the other big houses round about. He is quite good at arranging charabancs for us and he and his cronies do an awful lot for the poor."

Charles let him chatter on. He was tired and he wanted some dinner. Robert read his thoughts.

"Come on, I'll get one of the lads to take you to the kitchens" he said "I am sure Mrs. Cooper has something nice for you to eat. I think I smelt some stew cooking earlier on."

The idea of some stew livened him up a bit and he was happy to have one of the lads show him the way. "I'll see you in the morning" shouted the Head Gardener behind them.

"I'm Bill" said the young lad who had been delegated. He reminded Charles of himself five years ago. They walked across the lawns and into the huge kitchen where Mrs. Doris Cooper, a very large lady, was waiting for them plus a couple of Kitchen Maids who were hurrying to finish for the day.

"What is it about Cooks" thought Charles to himself "that they are always large – must be the cooking."

"Come in my lads and sit yourselves down." Mrs. Cooper chivvied a Kitchen Maid up to serve Charles and Bill with some stew and home made bread. It was really good.

"This will do for me!" said Charles as he cleared his plate. "Thank you very much."

Back at the Bothy Charles unpacked his bags and Bill immediately spotted the accordion.

"Wow, can you play that thing?" he exclaimed.

"Yes, I can after a fashion," grunted Charles.

"Cor, give us a tune, go on" cried Bill.

Charles obliged with a quick burst of 'Onward Christian Soldiers'.

"You will be popular" his new friend laughed. "Can you do some of the Music Hall songs?"

"Yes, but I need to sort myself out for now. Maybe another time. Tell me about my new employer."

"Well you will be popular" Bill repeated "and you will go down a treat at the Christmas party at Easthampstead Park."

Charles wasn't interested. He wanted to know about his employer.

"He's a Freemason" whispered Bill when he could see Charles fold the squeezebox together and put it in its case. "I don't know what it means really but they have some funny old customs and it seems to be a club for the posh and they do good things for the poor. He's a Knight Templar which means he has to believe in the Christian religion as well."

JOAN BLACKBURN · *Before the Rainbow* ~ 51

Charles believed in the Christian religion so that was all right in his book though he had never heard of it before either and nor did he know what a Freemason was.

"He is also the High Sherriff of Berkshire" went on Bill, pleased that he had Charles's attention. "and... he is a Justice of the Peace."

Well his new employer was nothing, if not, interesting. Charles had learned more about Charles Keyser in five minutes than he did about Lord Brownlow at Belton House in five years!

When Bill had finished his nattering Charles decided to write home to his mother and father. It might be some while before he saw them again. He was a little bit further away this time. But he now would be one of the Assistant's to the Head Gardener and it did bring with it more money, and after all 'it didn't grow on trees.'

Easthampstead Park 1906

"Did you see the master today?" said Ethel. "Honestly, he gets worse. I have just seen him riding around the grounds driving a fire engine."

Nothing surprised anybody downstairs in Easthampstead Park these days. His Lordship was quite a character and, owing to the fact that he was one of the richest men in Britain he could do practically anything he wanted. They had their own fire service within the grounds and so if his Lordship wanted to drive a fire engine then his Lordship could do so. Alice laughed and helped Ethel with some of the washing up that was piling up in the sink. It wasn't her job but she didn't mind helping if she had nothing else to do. After all she had been a Scullery Maid once herself. Now though she had worked her way up, just like her sisters had done. True, for a while she had been in peril of having to leave her job when his Lordship got

Lord Downshire driving the fire engine.

a divorce and Lady Katherine left, but fortunately they kept her on as Parlour Maid and Lord Downshire was always bringing new young ladies home. Now, it was likely that she would soon be a Lady's Maid again because he was engaged to be married to a lady by the name of Evelyn Foster.

"Where, where?" cried Betty, "where is he driving a fire engine?" Both girls ran out of the kitchen door falling over each other in the process.

"Oi! Don't you be long!" called Mrs. Brown, the Cook. "Jobs to do, jobs to do."

Alice followed them out and they were joined by some of the stable lads just in time to see his lordship driving the horse driven vehicle along the drive. She thought it was hilarious,

"If he doesn't come in soon he is going to get very wet" said Alice looking up at the grey clouds. "Winter is approaching."

They all watched fascinated until the contraption disappeared around the corner and Mrs. Brown became more agitated.

"Enough, you will see him on that thing again I have no doubt!" she called. "Come and get on with your jobs."

◆ ◆ ◆

DESPITE THE 'UPS AND downs' she had enjoyed working at Easthampstead Park for the past five years but still she hadn't met anybody to take her up the aisle. Not that she was worried much. Other people seemed to be more worried than she was. Both her younger sisters Edith and Emily were married now and older brother Joshua had been so for a long time.

"Come on Alice, it's time you got on with it" her twenty-one year old sister Laney had said to her.

"Oh, I just haven't met the right one Laney" she replied. "and if I don't I don't."

"Oh, just because she has done so she thinks everybody has to!" thought Alice to herself, but she did have to admit that at twenty-seven she was getting old compared to most young girls. One thing was for sure though, she fully intended to marry for love and if the right one did not come along then so be it. It wasn't that she lacked admirers, she didn't, but she was not really drawn to any of them. In the meantime, with the exception of the awful tragedy of young Jenny and the boiling water, it had been fun working for Lord Downshire. She had even been with the household to Hillsborough Castle in Northern Island where his Lordship had played host to King Edward when he went to unveil the imposing statue of Queen Victoria.

The journey itself had been an adventure and then to see the huge estate, all of which was owned by somebody that just chose to call himself Arthur Hill, was surreal to say the least.

But Arthur Hill was Lord Downshire and he could do what he wanted. Well almost. She smiled ironically to herself as she made her way to the Drawing Room to tidy up. He had got into some scrapes, that man. In fact she pulled herself up short, because it was no smiling matter. On another trip to Ireland he had got so carried away with driving motor cars that he accidentally knocked a young girl over and she later died.

"It's a miracle he didn't get done for manslaughter" James Chapman said when the news broke and it was all over the paper. He brought the newspaper into the kitchen and everybody read about it. The girls name was Elizabeth McGee.

"It says here though that he was only going at six miles an hour", said James, "and he did sound his horn constantly." Alice had heard that horn and she vouched that it could wake the dead so maybe the girl was just not used to cars being on the road. In any event he got away with it and escaped, what could have been, a long jail sentence, or worse.

No, life was never boring at Easthampstead Park! Now, Christmas was approaching and they would be hosting parties for all the servants that worked in the large estates round about. This was something that his Lordship allowed every year and it was great fun because it gave servants a chance to meet others besides those they worked, and lived with, day in and day out. Invitations would be going out soon to place like Highclere Castle and Aldermaston House among others. Alice was used to such functions but this time it would change her life.

CHAPTER V

The Right One

Alice swapped her Maid's uniform for her best floral dress with lace collar on the occasion of the Servant's Christmas Ball. She had enjoyed the function every year and she didn't expect this year to be any different. She shared a room with a new Parlour Maid called Annie and the younger girl watched as Alice brushed her shiny black hair which was her crowning glory.

Already they had heard the charabancs arrive and the laughter of people as they clambered out and made their way to the sumptuous Ballroom. Of course, quite a few of the staff had to be on duty for the occasion and it had been hard work but Alice was lucky as this time it was her turn to be the one being 'looked after'.

"Oooh, is this how the other 'arf live?" said Annie as they walked along the corridor and up the stairs to where somebody was already livening things up with, what sounded like an accordion.

Cook had done everybody proud with ample food and already things were well underway. There was a band but just at the moment there was a bloke on a squeezebox 'doing a turn' and he was playing a waltz. She and Annie sat down at the side of the room but she hadn't been there long before one of the grooms that had been chasing her for months asked her for a dance. She didn't really want to. She was quite happy to listen to the bloke on the accordion, but it was also rude to refuse so she got up and let him clasp her in a waltz. He smelt of sweat and cigars.

"I must say you are looking lovelier than ever," said Walter as he swung her around the room.

"How kind" she answered, but her mind was not on his attentions.

Instead, she felt her eyes drawn towards the young chap playing the music. He was so brown and weathered and, at the moment, he had such a lovely smile and his eyes twinkled as she danced past. She was drawn to his eyes which seemed to be greyish blue and, very, very cheeky. Walter was completely oblivious to the fact that he didn't have her fullest attention and just chatted on.

After he showed her back to her chair she politely made it clear that she wanted to sit it out for a while. With his ego sadly in tatters, Walter moved away and she turned her attentions to the young man with the accordion as he left the stage and went and joined his friends. Ethel and Annie sat down with her.

"Who's the bloke on the squeezebox?" said Alice.

"New gardener at Aldermaston I think" said Ethel "he's good on that squeezebox isn't he."

Meanwhile, taking a break from the music, Charles was asking his friend Bill a similar question. "Who is that beauty with the black hair over there?" he asked, nodding in the direction of Alice and Annie.

"Ha ha, way out of your league my man!" laughed Bill. "That's Alice Jones, the Lady's Maid – a bit older than you my friend and out of your league."

Charles felt a little bit deflated. Bill was probably right. He was still laughing.

"Yes, way out of your league!"

"All right old man, so you said that twice already!" grunted Charles. Nevertheless, he had learned to dance and could do a credible waltz so he promised himself that nothing ventured was nothing gained. In any case he was not going to have Bill tell him that she was out of his league any more. The Band were playing now and he had only just done a 'turn' on the squeezebox because he had been nagged to death by Bill. He got up and put the instrument down at the table occupied by some of the Aldermaston staff and walked boldly over to Alice as the musicians began a lovely slow waltz. If she turned him down then he was prepared for it. He could go back to Aldermaston and never see her again but at least he would never live to regret not asking.

"Can I ask your hand for this dance?" he said gruffly and suddenly, unlike him, he felt very shy. To his utter surprise she stood up and nodded to her friends.

"Why yes, thank you. I would love to" she said. He put his arm around her slim waist and swirled around the room much to the surprise of Bill who could just look on. *"Thank goodness for those dance lessons with Mother at the Church Hall!"* he said to himself. Somehow she felt right in his arms. She may be 'out of his league' but she felt right. She certainly didn't natter non stop like that other Alice that had chased him all over Belton when he had been there. *"Hm, pity she has to be called Alice,"* he said to himself, and then out loud, he heard himself saying. "My name is Charles. I would love to see you again if I may – on my next day off."

"Maybe I will" she laughed, "maybe I will." She had taken to this young man. He was clearly a rough diamond, but she reckoned he was a diamond for all that and she wanted to see him again.

They spent the rest of the evening together and all too soon it drew to a close. All Bill could do was look on in amazement that this new chap could catch such a beauty.

"I will write to you" said Charles when they sat close together between dances. "I know" he suddenly had a thought, "I will get a bike and I will cycle here on your next day off and take you for a walk somewhere."

Alice laughed "Ha ha, we are in the middle of winter Charles, you can't ride all over here on a bike!"

"You just watch me!" he said.

"Do you want to see the Menagerie before you go" Alice suddenly said. "Did you know that his Lordship even has a Menagerie in the house?"

"Well" said Charles "I suppose the richest man in England can have whatever he wants," but he wasn't prepared for what met his eyes. He followed her along the corridors of the palatial home to the Orangery and there, in huge cages were the monkeys and, further along, on his own, a brown bear. Charles was horrified.

"Poor bloody things" he exclaimed. "That's disgusting."

"I know" said Alice ignoring his language, "but they are well looked after – you can see they are."

It was true. Charles could see that their coats were shiny and they had plenty of food, but all the same he was still horrified, especially on behalf of the bear. It did mean they could be alone for five minutes though.

He put his arm around her and could smell the freshness of her newly washed hair. She was mesmerised by his kind grey eyes which were so opposite to his gruff exterior. He gave her a tentative kiss but stopped there. He didn't want to take liberties. She, in turn, respected him for that. All too often the female staff were subjected to unwanted advances from young men who thought they were easy game. Slowly, they walked back to where the dancing was ending and everyone was getting ready to get the charabanc home.

"I have a day off next week" said Alice suddenly.

"Then I shall write to you and I shall come and see you" said Charles. He gave her a peck on the cheek and followed all the staff from Aldermaston to the waiting bus. He turned round and waved and she waved back.

"You know she is five years older than you don't you?" whispered Bill as they settled down on the bus.

"I don't care" said Charles, "she is the one for me, and I am going to get her. Do you know anyone who has a bike I can borrow?"

They ended up laughing but Charles meant it. He would get his father to sell his bike and he would purchase another one with his savings. In the meantime he would borrow one.

"My brother has a bicycle" said the still laughing Bill, "I can ask him if you like, but I still say she is out of your league!" He just dodged the friendly cuff that Charles gave to his ear.

Back at Aldermaston life went on. Charles Keyser did not trouble them too much – he was too busy with his business interests and his duties as Mayor of Aldermaston. Nevertheless there was plenty to do and Charles Ratcliff entered into it with a new gusto.

"I see somebody has a twinkle in his eye" said Doris Cooper, the Cook, when he went into the kitchen for his lunch the following day. "I saw you eyeing up that pretty Housemaid at Easthampstead Park."

"I'm going to marry her." Charles announced. Everybody in the kitchen laughed.

"Ha ha, you've got some hopes" giggled Violet the Scullery Maid. "Good gracious, you have only just met her!"

"Well, any old how, I am going to write to her" he retorted.

"Good luck to you my boy" laughed Mrs. Cooper, humouring him "I know, I have some nice writing paper which I shall give you." She paused for a minute. "Oh, can you write?"

"Of course I can damn well write" grunted Charles. In fact his father had made sure that all his children had good educations and he could write and spell very well. Suddenly he was very glad that his father had been so insistent.

He took the writing paper and went back to the Bothy to write, what would be, the first letter of many between Aldermaston Court and Easthampstead Park.

EASTHAMPSTEAD PARK

"I'll bet you don't hear from him again" said Betty when the girls gathered in the kitchen the following morning. "He's only a young 'turnip top'."

"I don't care" said Alice. "He is a nice 'turnip top' and I took to him. He just struck me as being reliable and I bet I do hear from him."

They were interrupted by the Chief Housemaid chasing the staff to get on with their work. There was much clearing up to do after the party yesterday. Now the house had to be made ready for gentry to visit.

"I hear the Marquess is planning to marry Lady Evelyn next year" said Betty as they made their way to the Drawing Room. "I expect things will be different then."

Alice wasn't really listening to Betty's chattering. She was wondering if she would hear from Charles again.

A couple of days later a letter arrived and was passed on to her by one of the Footmen.

"Looks like that bloke was true to his word Alice" he remarked.

She flew into her room and ripped it open. He had certainly been true to his word. She knew he would. It was a lovely letter in beautiful writing.

"Well" she thought "the 'turnip top' has been well educated, and that's a fact."

The letter informed her that he had acquired a bicycle and that he was prepared to cycle the twenty or more miles to come and see her next week.

She ran down the corridor and knocked on the Housekeeper's door. Mrs. Lily Harris was in overall charge of all the staff and Alice knew that if she wanted to have her day off to co-incide with Charles then she would have to speak nicely to her.

"I'd like to change my day off Mrs. Harris, if I may" she said, when the imposing figure opened the door. She was tall with grey hair and wearing her black day dress with white starched collar. She looked at the letter in Alice's hand.

"I see, you have heard from that young man after all" she grinned.

"Good lord" thought Alice "Everybody knows my business – how news travels."

"Cook told me." She went in and looked at her diary of household events. "Yes, you can swap with young Angela."

Alice didn't have a clue who Angela was. There could be up to fifty staff in and around the house, not including the gardeners, at any one time. She didn't know all of them, but she didn't care. She had a feeling that Charles would turn up whether she had the day off or not but it would be nice to have the time to walk out even if it was cold and wintertime. She quickly wrote back and handed the letter to one of the footmen to post for her.

As soon as the letter had gone she pulled herself up short. What on earth was she doing? Why was she so taken with this young man who was nearly five years her junior? Yet he hadn't seemed like a young man. She had wanted to fuss over him and yet she felt as though he was in control. In any home he would be the boss but, only because she allowed him to be because she didn't mind it being so.

"Oh Alice, you are getting ahead of yourself here" she told herself. "He is probably one of the country bumpkins from Aldermaston having a laugh." But, she couldn't stop herself from hoping that he would indeed call on her. There was over twenty miles between the two households and if he was coming by bicycle, as he said he would do, then she would soon see how keen he was.

In fact Charles arrived at exactly the time he said he would. Alice was impressed that he had taken the trouble to wax his moustache and that he was wearing a high starched collar with his jacket and topcoat despite the journey on the bicycle. She was waiting for him at the Servant's entrance when he arrived, puffed out and quite cold. At least the weather was dry but it was extremely chilly. It occurred to her that he must have started out exceedingly early because the clock had not struck ten o'clock yet. Immediately though, she felt at ease in his company. She told him where to house his bicycle and then took him into the kitchen where the scullery maids fussed around and Cook found some bread and cheese.

"Come, sit by the kitchen range and get warm" said Alice.

"Oh I am made of strong stuff" said Charles but he still took her up on her offer.

It was too cold to go out for much of a walk so Cook suggested that once Charles had warmed through that she should take him to the Orangery, where they could have some privacy.

"Go on, off with you" said Cook "I'll get Daisy to bring you in some tea."

The Orangery was a large room with huge windows where the monkeys and the bear were kept. Charles hated the idea of keeping them like that.

"Look at them, poor things" he said as they walked into the room. He walked over to the bear who was busy chewing on some leaves. "Hello you poor old thing. You shouldn't be here should you?"

Alice stood back amused while he had a conversation with all the animals. She loved him already.

"I shouldn't worry about them much longer" she reassured him. "As I understand it, the new lady in his Lordship's life does not like them either. There is talk that they will go to a zoo."

Charles grunted and sat down.

They spent a while telling each other about themselves. Alice told Charles about her brothers and sisters.

"We have Joshua, and Edith, and Emily, oh and Annie, but nobody calls her Annie. We all call her Laney. Also there is my young brother Frederick Charles, only we call him Charlie."

"On the subject of names" replied Charles bluntly "I don't like the name Alice, it reminds me too much of that young clap-trapper that was chasing me in my last job."

Most people would have been offended but Alice laughed.

"Well it's not my fault that I was christened Alice, it's a popular name and what I was christened with. You can't just change it because you don't like it."

"Ah! replied Charles, "Ah, but you have just now finished telling me that your sister Annie is called Laney and your brother Frederick is called Charlie. What is good for the goose is good for the gander. I shall call you Kate."

"Kate!" laughed Alice. "*Cheeky devil*" she thought. "*We'll see about that!*" She wasn't quite sure if he was joking or not but he did have a point about the names in her own family!

Before the conversation went any further, one of the maids came in with a tray of tea.

"Cook says if you come to the kitchen when the bell goes for the upstairs people to have their lunch, she will give you some pie and vegetables" she said.

Charles was happy with that. Already it was worth the journey, but he would leave early this afternoon because he did want to get back before it got too dark. Many of the roads were unlit and you could not see a hand in front of your face. He did not want to end up in a ditch and there might be vagabonds about.

By the time it came for him to leave they felt as though they had known each other for years and Alice knew, that despite the fact that they came from different parts of the country and that he was a 'turnip top' and she a 'townie', they were made for each other. She wasn't too sure about being called Kate though but soon learned that it was a term of endearment rather than a change of name. Over the next few months she realised that he called her Alice when he was annoyed about something, and Kate when he was feeling happy.

"I don't care what he calls me" she said to young Lily "as long as he calls me."

In the meantime, Lord Downshire married Lady Evelyn Foster and Alice found that she was a Ladies Maid once again. Moreover, the Menagerie was removed to a zoo as everyone suspected it would be.

"I can't have a bear and monkeys in my Orangery" the new Marchioness declared. "Whatever next? Either they go or I go." So that was that!

◆ ◆ ◆

OVER TIME ALICE AND Charles were able to arrange their days off so that she could take him on the train to visit her family in Barnes, just outside of London. She had been away so long and was amazed at how much young Charlie had grown up. He was sixteen now and just starting out in the Civil Service helping with translating. Charles immediately took to him as he did with the rest of the Jones family. Alice's father, Joshua Kirck, in particular was very much a member of the Church just as his parents were. He, in turn, was impressed by the strong, honest and straightforward man that his daughter had fallen in love with.

Visiting the Ratcliff family up in Northampton was a much greater journey but they did it by train so that Elizabeth and John could meet Alice. None of them would ever get over the death of young Rosa, but life did go on and Elizabeth took them both to one of her Salvation Army meetings and Charles was able to take a turn on the accordion.

Then there was a visit to see Joseph, who was now a Master Baker, and take tea with him and Emmie and their young children.

"You watch out for that brother of mine" said Joseph. "He needs a good woman."

"They are a lovely family Charles" said Alice as they left the house and got the bus back to Pitsford. "Such delightful children." Later, they enjoyed a happy evening with Emily and young Mabel and even young John, and his new lady friend Maud, managed to find time to come and see this new lass that his brother had brought home.

All that remained was to get his father to sell his old bicycle.

"I shall buy a new one when I have saved up enough" he said to his father.

"Here son, you take this." Elizabeth emptied out a pot where she had been saving her lace money and gave some to Charles. She gave him fifteen shillings.

"Let that start you on your way."

It was the equivalent to a weeks wages.

"I can't take that amount Mother!" he exclaimed.

"Yes you can. You can save some as well" she replied. "Spend a little, save a little."

Alice fell in love with the simple and straight forward family and was fascinated by the skills shown by Elizabeth with her lace making. The two ladies became locked in conversation about the merits of one stitch over another while the men chatted about the best time to plant runner beans.

One person who was still totally shocked at the turn of events was Bill upon his return to Aldermaston.

"Honestly old chap" he said to Charles when he finally arrived back at work. "I genuinely thought she was out of..."

"I know," interrupted the young gardener with a smile. "Out of my bloody league!"

CHAPTER VI

Wedding Bells, 1908

Charles persevered with his courtship for nearly two years, during which time there were changes at East-hampstead as Lord Downshire finally married Evelyn. One thing that Alice was pleased about was that his Lordship began to lose interest in going over to Hillsborough in Ireland and he started renting it out permanently. There was talk that it would eventually be sold to the Government. It suited her because it was hard enough trying to meet up with Charles as it was without the further encumbrance of having to go away for months at a time just whenever it took her employer's fancy. Of course it was exciting to go there and she had enjoyed it but now the novelty had worn off.

At Aldermaston Charles continued to help oversee the gardens and he learned much from Robert Roache including keeping bees and even growing tobacco. Although Charles Keyser had plenty of money he preferred the home grown tobacco from the gardens and it was a skill to dry it out and chop it all up to make it just as he liked it.

Eventually he was able to buy a bicycle of his own and return the one he had been borrowing to Bill's brother. This in itself was an improvement because it had rubber tyres which made it easier and faster along the road and it also had a light driven by dynamo.

"We can't carry on like this though Kate" Charles said to Alice on one of his last trips before the wedding. "We shall have to find ourselves somewhere so that we can get married and be together. I'll get Bill to help me find somewhere."

Then of course there was a letter to write, to his friends Henry and Daisy. It was just as well that he did because news came that the pair of them were moving on and going to live back in Daisy's home town of Manchester. He was also still talking about joining the Army.

"Silly bugger!" thought Charles, "What the devil does he want to do that for when he has a wife and family?"

So much was happening, both in their own lives and in the world in general.

In the meantime Alice herself had been making plans and she had to inform the Housekeeper, and the people she had been working with over the past six years, that she would have to leave. In some ways it would be a wrench, but in others not. Things had changed now. It seemed strange having a new Lady of the house in place of Katherine, whom she had become quite attached to, but also she had never really got over the shock of young Jenny falling into the boiling water whilst doing the washing. She felt that the screams would haunt everybody who was there for ever and she shuddered every time she had reason to go into the Scullery. Now she needed someone to look after her and she felt that Charles was the man to do it. The fact that he would insist on calling her 'Kate' was a small price to pay.

"Well none of us are surprised" said Cook "he is a nice young man – a bit rough and ready, but reliable and that is the most important my dear, and he clearly loves you, anyone with half an eye can see that."

Alice agreed. It was probably one of the reasons why she loved him back. He was dependable and never let anyone down. If he said that he was going to find them somewhere where they could be together then that is exactly what he would do.

He would be her rock – but only because she allowed him to be.

Charles and Bill scoured the papers between them, looking for an establishment that would be willing to take on a gardener and provide a tide cottage for a newly married couple. He visited the Agency in the village of Aldermaston but there didn't seem to be anything locally. Not even at Easthampstead where there was a queue of people waiting for the Tide Cottages.

"I don't know why I am helping you with this" said Bill as they looked through yet more papers for the umpteenth time. "I don't really want you to go – I have got used to you around here you old cove."

Charles slapped him on the back.

"Well that's what happens when I bat above my league Bill."

Finally it was the Agency that found them somewhere, across in East Sussex at Haywards Heath.

"Hayward's Heath?" cried Charles. "Why that's miles away isn't it?"

Mr. Peabody in the Agency took an Atlas from out of a drawer and showed him where Haywards Heath was on the map.

"Oh well" sighed Charles "it looks like I am getting ever nearer to the seaside and that will be good for our health if nothing else."

"It's on the Beech Hurst Estate and they have huge gardens" said Mr. Peabody writing down the address for him. "There is a small furnished cottage that goes with the job. All you will need is your linen.

The couple arranged to stay with Joshua and Sarah for a couple of days. Behind closed doors Alice had the chance to try on the wedding dress that her Mother and sisters Laney and Edith were making for her. She was thrilled with it. It was made of white lace and pulled in at the waist and high at the neck. There was a large net hat that fitted just right on her thick hair.

"Thank you all of you" she looked at her slender waist in the mirror. "My goodness I had better be careful what I eat for the next few days" she laughed.

Eventually they caught the train to Haywards Heath for an interview with the owner of Beech Hurst, one Henry Mansfield-Knight. It was a lovely part of the country and Alice liked it. If Alice liked it then Charles liked it and that was that.

All that remained was to return to their respective employers for a few more days. Not that Lord Downshire or Charles Keyser were any the wiser. They were hardly ever in the huge establishments that they owned. Charles Keyser was very much involved with his Masonic Lodge and with the restoration of the Parish Church in Aldermaston. As for Lord Downshire? Well, as Cook would say, "you never know what his lordship would get up to next." Alice was answerable to the Chief Housemaid and Charles to Robert Roache, the Head Gardener.

Lady Evelyn was a bit disconcerted though. She had got used to Alice looking after her and helping her with her hair and buttoning up her dresses.

"I'll miss you Alice" she said when it became clear that she was really leaving. "Nobody will pin my hair up as well as you."

It was the household staff of both large estates who were the most closely affected though and, at the two separate establishments owned by two separate millionaires the send offs were similar.

At Aldermaston Court there were slaps on the back and cries of "well done old son" and "good luck old boy" plus an extra heartfelt embrace from Bill.

"I still reckon she is out of your league" he joked.

Charles put his bag on his back and rode his bike away from his friends and towards the station. All that remained was to put it in the Guards Van and travel to London where he would be staying with Alice's older brother Joshua and his young family.

Further up the country, in Northamptonshire, the Ratcliff family had heard the news of the forthcoming nuptials and plans were afoot to attend the wedding of their son Charles to Alice Jones.

At Easthampstead Park Alice waited on Lady Evelyn for the last time. She was a nice woman with pretty blonde hair tied up in a large roll around her head, and she was right, Alice seemed to have the knack of doing it just as she wanted it. At first it had seemed a bit strange having a new lady to attend to but after all the years at Ringwood looking after Lady Normanton, and now here, she had got used to changes and the vagaries of the gentry.

"Good luck to you my dear, and may your marriage be long and happy."

"Longer than his Lordship's previous one I hope" thought Alice.

She received a kiss on the cheek and a hug before going downstairs to where most of the staff were gathered to send her on her way. There were the kitchen staff and the upstairs staff together with the grooms and stable lads, all gathered round and wishing her good luck.

"Good luck Alice my love" said Cook. Her eyes welled up and she hastily wiped her apron across her face.

"Come on Madam, your chauffeur awaits" called one of the grooms who had just come in from the stables.

She was certainly leaving in style as she had one of Lord Downshire's cars to take her as far as the station. The chauffeur helped her put her case in the back and then she rushed back to Betty and gave her a final hug.

"Come on, come on" flustered Cook. "You will miss your train."

"Don't fuss" Alice laughed. Then she turned back to Betty. She would miss her.

"Have a good life Betty and I promise I will write to you when I get settled." The young Parlour Maid that she had worked with for so long could not hold back the tears anymore. However the emotion of the moment was relieved by everyone's laughter as Alice apprehensively climbed up into the car. She had never been in one before. Whenever she had travelled with his Lordship's entourage in Ireland it had been by carriage.

"Oh well, here goes" she called. "If it's good enough for the master it is good enough for me." She held onto her hat as the car pulled away with a shudder from Easthampstead Park and towards a new chapter in her life.

◆ ◆ ◆

IN THE MEANTIME SARAH Jones, and together with Alice's sisters, made ready for a wedding and her father, a Lay Reader himself, arranged the ceremony with the Vicar, the Reverend Philip DeWaal.

A few days later, on 17th August 1908, they were married in St. Mary's Church, Barnes. Her father, Joshua Kirck Jones, proudly walked down the aisle with her on his arm and with Laney following holding a posy of violets. The rest of the family and friends watched as Joshua handed his beautiful daughter, in the lovely white lace wedding dress, to the gardener from Northamptonshire. He turned to receive her hand and the smile on his face seemed to go from ear to ear. He was wearing a smart dark suit and high starched collar.

"Do you Alice Edith Jones take Charles Ratcliff to be your lawful wedded husband, to love and to cherish until death you do part......?" The familiar words rang round the church.

"I do" said Alice clearly.

Sarah wiped away a tear that escaped down her cheek.

Also in the congregation, and wiping away tears, were Elizabeth and John Ratcliff with young Emily and Mabel, together with John and Emmie and Joseph and Maud. They had travelled down on the train to London especially for the ceremony.

All that remained was to sign the register and it would all be over and Alice Jones would be Mrs. Charles Ratcliff.

The bells rang out and then the carriages took everyone back to 82 Archway Street, Barnes for a reception. But it wasn't to be for long. Just time for a toast from Joshua...

"Please raise your glasses to Charles and Alice. A long life and a happy one my dears!"

Sarah and Alice's sisters busied themselves making the Ratcliff family feel at home and then Charles went and gave his mother and sisters a kiss.

"Thank you for coming all this way." he said.

"It's fun!" interrupted Mabel "we are staying at an Inn tonight and going back home in the morning."

"She thinks it is all a big adventure" laughed John.

"I don't know," said Elizabeth "all my children getting married off. I can't keep up with it." She had given the couple a beautiful white fine cotton bedspread for a wedding present. It was embroidered all over with white silk and edged in lace she made herself.

"There is a story behind this" she told Alice. "The Lace Company were making it as part of an order for the old Queen and then, as you know, she died and it was all cancelled when only half done. I was given this when I left and I finished off the embroidery and the edging."

"It's beautiful!" exclaimed Alice. "I promise I shall look after it."

She ran into the bedroom with her sisters and changed into her going away dress with a three quarter length coat over the long skirt.

"Alice," whispered Emily "why does he call you Kate all the time?"

"Ha ha" giggled Alice, "because I let him. It's his way of saying 'darling' I think. He is not a great one for fine words."

"Oh!" said Emily not really convinced.

"Well, as he pointed out to me" smiled Alice, "we call Frederick 'Charlie' and we call Annie 'Laney'! I didn't have a leg to stand on."

The conversation ended as always, when the sisters were together, in laughter.

The new Mr. and Mrs. Charles Ratcliff were driven by young Joshua to Clapham Junction and there they, together with their luggage, including the bedspread and one 'well used bike', boarded the train to Haywards Heath and, what was hoped, would be a long life together.

"Good luck sister" said Joshua as she leaned out of the window to wave to him.

"And to you brother, and to you."

Nobody knew it at the time, but in a few years time the storm clouds would appear that would affect everybody in the country.

CHAPTER VII

Haywards Heath, 1908-15

The birds were singing and, just for once, Charles did not complain about a cockerel waking him when he and Alice woke up in Beech Hurst Cottage on Butlers Green Road. It was more modest than Easthampstead and Aldermaston but it was all working out well and Alice was happy enough to be working as Parlour Maid for Lady Mansfield-Knight. She watched Charles as he scoffed down his porridge and toast before striding off across the fields to where he would be helping maintain the gardens. He was a gardener through to his fingertips and she could not imagine him doing anything else.

As far as her job was concerned, her Ladyship was quite happy to employ her but was well aware that there was every possibility that the couple would have children.

"After all, you are not getting any younger" she reminded Alice. "You don't want to leave it too late."

"Anyone would think I had a choice in the matter" thought Alice who was well aware that, at twenty-nine, time was not on her side.

She loved her first home. Although tiny, there was enough room for them and a spare room for any children. It was sparsely furnished but she knew that, with a few feminine touches, it would be comfortable and would suit them.

They got to know the couple in the Tide Cottage next to theirs who were Bert the chauffeur and his wife Muriel.

"Don't worry my dear" said Muriel when Alice confided her fears to her about her age. "If God wants you to have children then children you will have."

However, Christmas came and went and there was still no sign.

"Don't be impatient" said Muriel when she came round for a cup of tea and a gossip. It's early days yet. You take no notice of her nibs up the house telling you to get on with it."

Then in March the following year Alice started to have her suspicions. She was feeling queasy in the mornings and there was no sign of her 'monthlies'. She swore Muriel to secrecy. "I want to be sure Muriel. I will go to the Doctor and make sure."

She walked down the road in the spring sunshine to see Doctor Roberts but she all but ran all the way back.

"You are at least two months pregnant young lady" he had informed her "your baby will be due next November if my sums are right."

Alice felt that her happiness would know no bounds – being told she was pregnant and being called a 'young' lady all in the same sentence!

Charles was beside himself with joy and both of them settled down that evening to write to their respective families. Charles also wrote to Henry who he had originally been with at Althorp House and who had dragged him off to Lincolnshire in the first place, much to his mother's disgust. Who knows how things would have turned out if he had not gone with Henry? He might never have gone to Aldermaston and his life would have been very different.

The couple had a few days of excitement and planning for the baby before their happiness was cut short by events up in Northampton that were out of their control Instead of the joyous letter that Charles expected to get back from his mother about being a grandparent again, it was one full of grief. She was delighted with news of the baby of course, but she had to tell him that young Emily was very ill with TB and not expected to recover.

"Oh not again!" exclaimed Charles when he read the letter. He threw it across the room in his rage. "She is just sixteen Alice, the same age as young Rose was."

Alice tried her best to comfort him but it was no good, he was angry as well as upset.

"It's no good I am going to have to go. I'll see his Lordship now and try and get some time off".

The fact that he called her Alice showed how angry he was. He stormed out of the house and she watched from the window as he strode towards the big house to see Mr. Mansfield-Knight. She waited, not knowing whether to run next door to Muriel or to try and do some housework. She was in floods of tears. Little Emily, who she had last seen just last year at her wedding! It was unbelievable and yet so many were dying with TB. It was so common. If she went down to the village there was always somebody who had lost a loved one. It was common for people to lose as many as three or four children in one family.

The sound of the gate banging shut told her he was back.

"He has given me three days Kate." Clearly he was beginning to calm down.

"I'll come with you" said Alice. "I'll go and get our bags packed."

"No you won't!". You can't go frolicking around the country-side on steamy old trains. I'll go and I will be back immediately"

"Charles, I am only a couple of months pregnant. See I am hardly showing. I will be all right. This time, I am the boss and I am coming with you."

"Oh what a wicked blow" thought Alice "to lose two sisters at the same age and just sixteen years old."

Alice usually allowed Charles to be in charge, but not this time and, just for once, he was happy for her to take control.

He made another trip to Beech Hurst house to get permission for them to lose their Parlour Maid as well as their Gardener for three days. "Not that it makes a lot of difference to them" he thought "I'll not have her working once the baby gets bigger."

It was a long journey for them both, firstly into London and then across on the Underground that so put him in mind of being a pesky mole, and then the journey to Northampton. All the time he prayed that they would be on time and Alice clung to his hand to calm him down. They arrived just in time to see Emily before she went to sleep for ever.

Charles and Alice settled down for a sad evening with the family. Then Charles waited for an appropriate moment to remind everyone that Alice was pregnant and that they had something to look forward to. It was the first time in the visit that he saw his mother give a watery smile.

"Yes it's wonderful news" she said "They say that if you shut one door another is sure to open. I just wish it wasn't overshadowed by our sadness." She kissed Charles. "You must look after this lovely wife of yours, you hear me son?"

He endured the slaps on the back from his brothers and father amid cried of "well done old chap" and the girls gathered around Alice. For a brief, a very brief, moment the sadness of the occasion was slightly relieved.

Emily was due to be buried a few days later on 9th June. Charles and Alice would not be able to come back for that but he was satisfied that his two brothers and his father would support his mother and fourteen year old Mabel, who was, of course, distraught.

Time is a healer and other events in the outside world took Charles's mind off the death of his sister, albeit briefly. The way to learn about things was from the newspaper and he tried to see one most days.

"Oh goodness me, look at this Kate!" he laughed "Frederick Cody has made the first flight in an aeroplane in Britain."

"Frederick Cody? That's Buffalo Bill isn't it? Oooh it doesn't seem right to me. I have hardly got used to cars."

"Says here that 'Mr. Frederick Cody made his first flight on 16th October."

The world was changing very fast and so were their lives. A month later their little girl was born. They named her Rosa Alice after the sister that Charles had lost before Emily.

"If we have another little girl we will name her Emily" said Alice.

◆ ◆ ◆

CHARLES SETTLED INTO HIS job on the large Beech Hurst estate. He still though had an ambition to be a Head Gardener somewhere. This would do for now though and he had his lovely little daughter to come home to every evening. She was a bonnie baby with the dark eyes and hair of her mother. When he was trimming back hedges or pruning roses he often found himself pondering upon how things had changed over the years. The very idea of someone taking off in an aeroplane was just unbelievable when he was a lad. He was also interested in the art of photography and hoped to have a camera of his own one day. Then there was lots of talk in the papers about wireless and that soon you would be able to hear people speak to each other across the air waves. It was all fascinating stuff.

He heard back from his friend Henry with their new address in Manchester, but he confirmed that he had actually done what he had been saying he would do for some time. He was joining the Army!

"What!" exclaimed Charles as he read Henry's news. "I really didn't think he would do it."

"I've joined the Lancashire Fusiliers" he wrote "I want to see the world and this is the best way I know how before I am too old, and it is a way of providing for the family."

"Two old! He's nearly thirty! Silly bugger!" exclaimed Charles and threw the letter across the room.

"Charles!" cried Alice, "language in front of the baby!"

However, the baby slept, sweetly oblivious.

It was Alice that first heard about the death of the King. Somebody telegraphed the Post Office when she was in the Village and soon there were notices everywhere. "King Edward the Seventh has passed away, long live the King."

"Oh dear, he only had nine years on the throne, poor old chap," said Charles when he finally got his newspaper the following day. His mother lived so long."

The Coronation of King George the fifth and Queen Mary took place on 22nd June 1911, just four months before the birth of Charles and Alice's second child. The sadness at the death of the King was soon replaced by the joyous Coronation which, this time, could be seen in newsreels at the Cinema and in plentiful pictures in the Newspaper and Tatler magazine.

Times they were changing but, for Charles and Alice, nothing could surpass the arrival of their son who they named Stanley. It was October and the leaves were falling from the trees when the midwife came to the little cottage on Butlers Green Road and delivered the healthy baby. Just like his older sister he had a mop of dark hair but he had the blue/grey eyes of his father.

"We shall call him Stanley after the road where I was born in East Sheen" said Alice, "I like that name."

"Oh isn't he beautiful!" Muriel twittered when she came in from next door to see the new arrival. Two year old Rosa looked on in wonder and just wondered where he had appeared from.

Two years later, in 1913 their little girl Doris Emily was born. The Emily after Charles's sister who died, like Rosa, so tragically young. For the family, their lives seemed to be complete although, in the wider world, just a year before there had been such tragedy with the sinking of the Titanic. Even now, barely a day went by without the stories in the newspapers of the one thousand five hundred dead when the huge vessel hit the iceberg. There was still blaming and counter blaming by politicians and press alike. On the first anniversary of the tragedy, just before the birth of little Doris, the papers carried the list of names and there were memorial services in the churches throughout the country.

"I still can't believe it" said Charles as the little family walked back from Church. "That anyone could build a ship to carry two thousand or more passengers. The largest ships that I have ever seen were those puffing down the River Thames when we went to see your parents."

"I can't even imagine what two thousand people all in one place must look like" said Alice. She looked down at the little baby in her arms, "those poor little children and babies who lost their lives as well. Oh it is just dreadful Charles. I feel almost guilty that we are so happy."

In the little tide cottage it was a happy time with their three small children and nobody was aware that just one year later everyone's lives would change for ever. The clouds of war were looming ever closer.

◆ ◆ ◆

"Look at this" said Charles. Alice was busy trying to feed three little children, all under the age of five, who didn't particularly want to be fed. She did not want to look at the paper but she tried to show willing. "Look!" he went on "the Turks have been driven out of Southern Europe. Good job too. There seems to be so much unrest out there."

Alice wasn't really interested in what the Turks were doing. There did seem to be a lot of unrest though, and so many young men, like Charles's friend Henry were joining the Army in an attempt to see the world or to join in all the excitement of chasing away the Turks. Whenever she went into the village there was always somebody walking around in a khaki uniform. She was beginning to feel a little bit uncomfortable about it all and wondered if they knew just what they were going into.

So was Charles. The future did not appear to be very good at all. He began scouring the papers, not only to read about the events across what was, to him, the other side of the world, but to see if he could find a job nearer to Alice's family, just in case the unthinkable happened and Britain did go to war.

"But we are settled here and we have been happy" protested Alice, "Rosa is about to start school in the village."

"All the more reason Kate" he argued. "It's all the more reason to do it now while the children are young. It seems to be a very unsettled world just now."

Meanwhile events were rapidly unfolding in Europe and beyond while three little children gave in and ate their dinner.

Minds were taken off events abroad when news arrived that Alice's mother Sarah died on 2nd March 1914. The shock was almost too much to bear but it convinced her that Charles was right. It would be a good thing to move a bit closer to home so as to be near her widowed father. Of course he had Edith and Laney to look after him but she wanted to be part of his life too.

It was a sad family that journeyed up to Barnes for the funeral. Alice tried to be brave in front of the children but, behind closed doors, she wept. She couldn't imagine life without her mother in it.

The children were looked after by neighbours while Alice and Charles accompanied the rest of the family to the Parish

Church at Barnes where, just six short years ago they had married and it had been such a joyous occasion.

It was just three months later, on 28th June that news was received about the Archduke Ferdinand being assassinated by a Serbian. The accounts of the outrage were all over the newspapers and pinned to every shop window.

"Oh my lord!" said Charles "this will cause a war – you wait and see."

In fact countries were mobilising their troops and there was even talk that there would be conscription in Britain if things did not settle down.

Then came even more devastating News as far as Alice was concerned. Her brother Charlie had joined the Army as an interpreter!

"Whatever is he thinking of?" exclaimed Alice "He never would have done so if Mother had been around. All these posters of Lord Kitchener are turning the young ones heads."

"I doubt if she would have stopped him" said Charles, "he is a young man and maybe he wants to see the world, and some of these younger ones do join the Army to see the world." Deep down he had a feeling that he might be called upon to do his duty before long but he said no more.

Finally, the decision to move was taken out of their hands by Lady Mansfield-Knight. Her home was going to be commandeered for use as a possible hospital for soldiers should war be declared.

"Oh my God!" exclaimed Alice, "Oh my God! This really looks as though things are bad!" Things were going from bad to worse. One did not know what to expect next.

Charles was determined to get Alice back to Surrey and, with the help and influence of his employer he was able to find just such a position. A Mr. Browne-Douglas of Redhill, Surrey needed an experienced gardener and a Tide Cottage would be provided. It was still a long way from Barnes but at least it was in the same county as Alice's family and, as it happened, marginally nearer his.

"Actually I don't blame you Ratcliff" said his employer "there are going to be a lot of changes and all of this estate is being sold to the Government. It looks like it is going to be used for wounded troops if we end up at war. There is so much unrest everywhere."

Charles was shocked but not surprised. Lord Mansfield-Knight was an old man and many of these huge estates were being sold off. The old order was changing fast and the large Estates that he and Alice had been used to working in were being sold on. He wrote to Mr. Browne-Douglas that evening and received a letter straight back inviting him to go for an interview.

The foreign news did not stop coming. Newspaper after newspaper carried the stories of what was going on in the wider world and even Alice started to feel vulnerable. Everywhere she went in the village she seemed to come face to face with the posters of Lord Kitchener calling young men to join the Army. The idea of just being in Surrey made her feel more secure. Surely they would not send Charles away though. Good lord, he was in his thirties now and with three children.

◆ ◆ ◆

THERE WAS CONSTANT TALK of conscription and even Mrs. Mansfield-Knight had something to say about it when she went into work taking the children with her.

"Oh it is a terrible thing Alice" she said "goodness knows where it will all end. I think there will be a war."

"I don't think it will affect Charles though!" said Alice, "after all, I don't think they would call up a man of his age. It's the youngsters they are after."

"Huh, nothing would surprise me," her ladyship grunted.

Charles received a letter straight back from Mr. Charles Christie Browne-Douglas's secretary inviting him to attend an interview at his home at Hillbrow, Nutfield Road.

Even as Charles caught the train there were posters all over the place announcing that Germany had declared war on France and that Belgium and Russia were mobilising their troops. He couldn't help feeling that he was preparing his family for the inevitable.

CHAPTER VIII

Redhill, 1914

It was a hot sultry August day when the little family left Haywards Heath. Bert from next door secured permission from their employer to use the car to carry them and their possessions to Redhill. Fortunately it was a large Rover with plenty of room for Alice and the children and also a good sized area for baggage space. But as they drove along the lanes towards Redhill it was impossible to ignore the hundreds of men in Army uniform marching in columns towards railway stations.

"It's not good Kate" said Charles. "I don't like the look of it at all." Unbeknown to them at the time, one hundred and twenty thousand troops were on their way to France.

Within five days of the family settling into their new home at Hillbrow, Redhill, on 12th August 1914, Britain declared war on Germany and Hungary. This also included the whole Commonwealth.

"It's a World War" exclaimed Charles "I bet old Henry wishes he had not joined the Lancashire Fusiliers now."

"And what about Charlie?" gasped Alice, "what about him? Well at least mother did not live to see it."

Charles didn't answer but he had to agree. He also knew that if he wasn't called up soon he would have to go and volunteer. He thought he would wait until they had settled in and then see what happens.

It was a nice cottage at Hillbrow and only a short walk from the main house. Alice busied herself settling in and found a school for Rosa to attend. Then she took the two youngest children in the pram to see Mrs. Jessie Browne-Douglas while Charles got to know his new employer. He still hoped that one day he would be a Head Gardener somewhere but, just for now, this would do. He hoped he would not be called up but one could never be too careful and he wanted Alice to be looked after.

"Oh what lovely children my dear" said Jessie as she cooed away at one year old Doris while three year old Stanley looked on with a faint air of boredom. There were plenty of other things for a three year old to do, like helping Father pull weeds out.

Jessie had two older daughters who had now left home and two, John and Archibald, who were at school.

"I'm used to having little ones about the place Alice, and now that mine are older I miss it. Yours will be most welcome if you want the job as Parlour Maid. You certainly have good credentials having worked for Lord Downshire." She paused .. "Lord Downshire eh! One of the richest men in Britain." She was clearly impressed.

And so it was that Alice secured the job of Parlour Maid in the Brown-Douglas household. She was able to take the children with her and they would play happily while she worked. She regretted having to move yet again – about her fifth move since she had left school but, in the event that Charles would have to go and fight, she would feel safer here and it was a bit nearer to her family.

The tales from the war kept appearing in the Newspapers. Russia had invaded Germany. German troops occupied Brussels. Older men like Charles viewed it all with trepidation whilst younger men like Alice's brother Charlie thought it was all one big adventure.

Autumn turned to winter at Redhill and still the newspaper reports were plentiful. Although there was talk, nobody in Britain knew exactly what was going on. It was known that reporters were taking photographs and trying to film but it was impossible to report the carnage that was happening. But bit by bit came news of the deaths of our soldiers. Alice would go into the village and there was always somebody that knew somebody who had lost a loved one. Charles was over thirty now, surely they would consider him to be too old?

♦ ♦ ♦

"IT'S NO GOOD, WE knew it was coming" said Charles when the conscription papers arrived in the late summer. Alice sank into the chair and wept. "I have to go or I will get shot as a deserter. Besides it is not for good yet. This is just for me to get issued with uniform and to do some training." Three small children looked on totally puzzled and wondered why their mother was so upset.

"I can't believe that they would call up a thirty-one year old man with three little children" she wailed.

"Maybe they have run out of young ones" he said wryly. "In any case Kate, I couldn't have gone on much longer without volunteering. I have to do my bit and I doubt if they will call my brothers up. After all, Joe is nearer forty than thirty."

Then she pulled herself together. Now it was time to show a stiff upper lip. The last thing he wanted was to have a quivering wreck of a wife when he was going off into the unknown. Her young brother was already out in Flanders somewhere. They would both come back safe. She would say her prayers and they would both come back safe.

"Oh well, I had better go and tell the boss that he is about to lose his gardener" said Charles. "Maybe we should leave here and get you back home with your father."

"No Charles, no." She cried. "I am sure Mrs. Browne-Douglas will let me stay on. What's the point of leaving here when you will be back in no time. Besides, my father is being well looked after by Edith and Laney. They haven't got room to take all of us."

"I will be happier if you are at home" he argued.

"No! It means we will both lose our jobs and it's almost like saying that we have given up and you are not coming back. No I will not have it."

When Alice put her foot down that was it, and even Charles could not argue with her. It was in the hands of their employers. In a way, he had to agree. She probably would be better here, where they had been in the past year since leaving Haywards Heath.

"Oh lord, I wonder how much longer we will have to move around before we become settled for ever!" he said to himself as he plonked his trilby hat on his head and strode off into the September sunshine. There would be much to do.

He strode across to the house deep in thought. He had never imagined himself as a soldier, much less hold a rifle, although he would shoot a fox if it came after the chickens. He was made of strong Northampton stuff, but even he found it hard to keep a stiff upper lip as he went to see the boss. What on earth would the next few months have in store? There seemed to be war everywhere, the Germans against the Russians, France and Britain against the Ottoman Empire. Where would he end up? He had never been abroad. As far as he was concerned 'abroad' was for foreigners. He was happy amongst the animals and the flowers. The world was never meant to be like this. He angrily brushed a stray tear away. It seemed like only five minutes ago that they had that lovely happy day when they got married. Now, who knows what to expect.

"Don't you worry my lad" said Mr. Browne-Douglas when Charles caught up with him. "We will take care of Alice." He wiped his feet carefully and just stepped inside the front hall as Jessie Browne-Douglas appeared from the dining room.

"Alice can still stay on here" she said. "I will be glad of her company."

"It's just for training at the moment" said Charles "hopefully I will be back in a month"

Now the time had come. For Alice it was the first time they had been apart and this was just for a few weeks. Supposing it was to turn into years? He reported for duty and spent the next few weeks getting rigged out with Army uniform and learning how to use a rifle correctly. It was decided that he would be a signaller so he had to learn how to send messages by using a lamp, Morse code and flags. He, along with hundreds of other men, stayed in tents and got to know about Army life from scratch. For him the time went quickly as there was so much to learn, but for Alice the time dragged by and every day seemed like a week. Then, finally, there was a last trip home before the whole Battalion was shipped off to Northern France. Alice rushed to greet him when he arrived back at the house, this time in the uniform of the West Surrey Regiment.

"He's a gardener!" she thought to herself "not a soldier."

The following day it was the 22nd November and one little girl was excited because she was six and had cake for tea, though she did think it strange that her father was dressed the same as all those soldiers she saw when mother took her to the shops. She thought it even stranger when he packed his bag, gave them all an extra big hug and kiss and said goodbye. Stanley and Doris just played with their toys but Rosa was old enough to know that something was not right, especially when her mother could not hold back tears any longer.

"You go Charles" said Alice "I don't want to watch you walking away. I want to see you when you come back."

He walked down the path and Rosa followed him. He picked her up and gave her another kiss.

"Happy birthday sweetheart" he said. "You enjoy the rest of your birthday." Then she watched him walk down the road until he was out of sight. She watched and she waited but he didn't come back.

Doris, Stanley and Rosa.

CHAPTER IX

'The Bit in Between'

"I AM GOING TO wake up in a minute and find it has all been a bloody nightmare" said Charles to his comrade Fred. "I am up a bloody tree. Who would have thought, six months ago, that I would be up a bloody tree!"

Fred sat on the wooden platform at the side of him and on the other side was a young Lieutenant who looked just as scared as they were. The engineers had built an observation platform high in the branches of a tree. It was in three stages with ladders connecting each level and the men were at the topmost one, acting as lookouts and sending signals further down the line. It was freezing cold despite the huge greatcoats they were all wearing and Charles had a vantage point to see the carnage of the battlefield just outside Ypres in all its glory. The trouble was that it probably would not be long before the enemy spotted them.

"I don't know which is worse" said Fred. "Being stuck up here like a target or being down there in all that bloody mud."

"Keep your eye on the enemy" commanded the Lieutenant "signal straight down the line if you see any movement forward".

Both men stopped their chattering and concentrated. They had a huge cumbersome heliograph set on a tripod with which to signal messages and a telescope to watch out for anything coming their way. Charles surveyed what, to him, was his idea of hell. All around him, as far as the eye could see, there was mud. Below him were the trenches with the soldiers shivering in the mess and sometimes with the mud falling in on them and burying them alive. Other soldiers were busy trying to pump out water. To Charles, it seemed to have rained every day since the Battalion had arrived to relieve the South Staffords who had marched back into friendly territory for a break. Well, some had marched, others had gone back in field ambulances or, where possible, taken back to lie in a mortuary somewhere.

Then a noise of an engine made them look up and a lone aeroplane flew overhead. Charles and Fred watched fascinated. Aeroplanes were more common now and being used in the war but, even so, it still took some getting used to seeing a thing flying around the sky that wasn't a bird or a balloon. Then, to their horror the pilot opened fire to the ground.

"Hey, that's not playing the white man!" shouted Fred.

Charles signalled down the line but somebody in the trenches had already spotted it and opened fire. Clearly there was a hit

because the aeroplane descended very rapidly. Then there was a shout from the German trenches. "Gentlemen, how are you?"

"Right chaps" said the Lieutenant "I think it is time we made a move from here." Charles and Fred dismantled the heliograph and the men scrambled down the three lots of ladders carrying their equipment between them.

"Damn this!" puffed Charles as they ran for the trenches and fell in the mud. Then the enemy opened concentrated artillery which lasted for over an hour. He lay in the filth and briefly wondered what his brother-in-law Charlie was up to and if he was OK. He was in this hell hole somewhere.

"If we have to run" cried Fred "I don't know how we are supposed to do so carrying all this lot."

The place was just a heaving mass of frightened men trying to do their duty. The horrifying thought was that it had been actually going on a year before they had even arrived there.

They were trying to keep the enemy back but it would not stay like this, sooner or later they would have to go over the top. Any ideas of staying up the tree were gone as it became blackened and scarred like the rest of the trees forward of their position. Except that some of them were not real trees! Some were man made hollow trunks with branches sticking out of the top. A man hid inside to fool the enemy and to get closer for observation. Nobody volunteered for that job in a hurry.

As darkness fell the guns went quiet and the tired and shattered men marched back into friendly territory for food and sleep to try and refortify themselves in order to repeat the same performance day after day. Most of the West Surrey's were billeted in a Tobacco Factory. They were exhausted and all Charles wanted to do was go home. But it was not to be. Between them they used whatever was available to cook some food for themselves. Stoves had been provided and they had chickens and vegetables bought in the villages behind the

Tree Observation Post.

friendly lines. They also had food parcels sent from home which they shared with each other.

Charles was pleased to see that one had arrived for him from Alice. She had put together a small parcel of biscuit, jam and cake and some of her own special hand made pastries.

"Well, that's more like it." he declared when he had eaten and washed. "Now I feel more like a human being."

Most of the Battalion were crowded into the large factory, that is, except for those that had been taken away in ambulances or shipped in boxes back to Calais, and soldiers had been detailed to dig trenches for latrines and build washhouses.

"Aye, this is all right for now" said another of his colleagues "won't be so easy when we get further forward though. There is talk that we will be going over the top soon."

Charles had got to the point where he couldn't care less. Anything had to be preferable to sitting up a bloody tree day after day.

"Oh well, we shall know soon enough I daresay" said Fred. Charles opened up the box containing the heliograph and checked that it was in good working order and then settled down in the hopes of getting some sleep despite the snoring of hundreds of men in and around the Factory.

When they awoke in the morning they were greeted with the news that the Battalion were, indeed, going 'over the top'.

Once again it was raining and once again they marched to what, for some of them, would be certain death. Everybody had fear in their eyes as they marched along and sang to try and calm the nerves. This time the heliograph was left behind and, instead, they took the lighter and less cumbersome Trench Signalling lamp which was battery operated. They all poured into the trenches and In the distance Charles could see the lumbering shapes of hundreds of tanks, like great slugs, sliding across the mud. The Artillery was in position and soon the order rang all along the lines. Everyone climbed out of the dug outs and moved forward. Fred and Charles ran together and it was like a firework display going off all around them. To the right and left of them men were screaming and falling. The soldiers ran blindly, hardly knowing where they were going and then fell head over heels into a bomb crater full of water.

"I think we might as well stop here" said Charles as more men including their Lieutenant, fell in with them.

After an hour they crawled out, slipping and sliding over each other in the process, only to be greeted by the sight of the dead body of a horse that had been ripped apart by the mortar fire. Then came the 'whiz-bangs' – rocket fire which whizzed across the sky and exploded like it was Guy Fawkes night. Overhead, British aeroplanes were shooting into the enemy lines. Charles had given up trying to be surprised at anything from now on. There was no time to ponder on how fast things had progressed since that day when Frederick Cody had flown for the first time in Britain.

Suddenly, as quickly as it had started, the enemy began to pull back. Clearly the Artillery had done its job and stopped the advance of the Germans. Now they could pull back into their own trenches until the next time. Then there was silence, apart from the cries of wounded men, as what was left of the Battalion walked back passing dead bodies to the right and left of them and stretcher parties came to retrieve what they could. Charles was ready to send any messages along the line.

"Looks like we have lived to fight another day" said their Lieutenant as they slipped back into their own lines.

"Another day! Thought Charles, "how many more days I wonder."

"Never mind" said Fred wryly, "Christmas is coming!"

DECEMBER 1915 – REDHILL

"Is Father back?" said Rosa as she came in from school and took her coat and boots off. Alice tried to smile and treat everything as if it was normal but it wasn't normal. She hadn't a clue when he would be hack, if at all but it was the question that her eldest daughter asked every day when she got home.

"No Rosa dear, not yet." She leant over Stanley and Doris who were attempting to draw pictures at the table and looked at their work. "Oh that is lovely Stanley, we shall have to see if Father Christmas can bring you some more crayons."

Rosa put her coat on again and went to the front door. Alice knew exactly where she was going. She was going to stand at the gate and watch for her father the same as she had done for the past fortnight.

"Put your coat on Rosa" she said to the six year old and don't be long. It's getting dark now. He won't be home today dear." She knew it was no good to try and stop her standing at the gate. Even the neighbours were used to it now and she would get bored and come in after a little while.

Rosa walked down the path and stood just outside the gate and looked down the long straight road that lead towards Redhill. She wanted to be the first to tell everyone that he was on his way, but there was no sign. Once she saw a man in uniform and ran towards him and then promptly ran straight back again when she realised it was not her father.

As Alice expected, she eventually grew tired and wanted her tea so she went back indoors.

"He's gone to be a soldier" said Stanley. "Father is a soldier now."

"I know!" retorted Rosa, "but I don't want him to be a soldier and he went down that road so he must come back down that road."

Alice was just grateful that she had the three children to take her mind off things but it was night time when it was worst. Once they were in bed and then she had time for her thoughts. It was impossible to escape the news of what was going on in Northern France, or further afield in the Dardanelles for that matter. It filled every newspaper and messages were coming to the Post Office by wireless all the time. There was even talk that one day in the future people would have a wireless in their house so they would know everything that was happening but she hoped to goodness it would all be over by then. The war had been on over a year now and the talk in Redhill was of nothing else and it seemed that everyone knew somebody who had lost a husband or a son or a brother. The Railway Station seemed to consist of hundreds of men in uniform going off to war whilst wounded men were being shipped back on a daily basis, and as everyone had suspected, the big houses were opening up as hospitals.

She also had the company of Jessie Browne-Douglas and it was nice to be able to take Stanley and Doris up to the house with her to play whilst Rosa was at school. Stanley would be at school the following year but she hoped to God that the war would be over by then.

Meanwhile Christmas was coming and she could knit socks. In fact, everyone was knitting socks for the troops and passing them on to the Red Cross or the Soldiers' Sock Fund so that the men could try and keep their feet warm in the trenches.

"Oh Alice" said Jessie, "why do we have to have wars? I don't even understand what caused this one."

"I don't think any of us do Madam" replied Alice. She looked across at little Doris who was playing happily in the huge play pen whilst Stanley busied himself trying to build a tower of bricks. "I just want the world to be a better place for them," she said.

"Don't we all Alice, don't we all?"

◆ ◆ ◆

IT WAS ALMOST CHRISTMAS Day when she finally received a letter from Charles. She recognised his beautiful writing straight away and couldn't open it fast enough. Even in the heat of battle, and under these nightmarish circumstances, he could make her laugh.

"They had me up a bloomin' tree Kate!" he wrote "up a bloomin' tree. Now I know what the crows feel like." She smiled to herself. She didn't know what he was doing up a tree, but at least he was alive. "The cooking isn't as good as yours. It's just bully beef all the time and we are living in a Tobacco Factory!" But it didn't tell her much. It was typical of him that he wasn't going to worry her or go into any detail of what he and his comrades were going through. She put it away carefully in the drawer in the bedroom and wondered where her brother was.

◆ ◆ ◆

SHE DID HER BEST for the children at Christmas. They sang carols round the Christmas tree and made paper chains which she hung round the room. She made the paste for the chains out of flour and water, which wasn't very successful, but it kept them all amused. She had taken a food parcel and some socks to the Red Cross so she hoped Charles would receive it, but if not him, some other poor soldier.

She thought of him and his old 'squeezebox' which had first brought them together. The children had hardly heard him play it as it had been stuck away in a cupboard, but he usually resurrected it at Christmas and played the carols. The children sang well though. Well at least Rosa and Stanley did. Doris tried.

"Come on, come on now" she said "drink your cocoa and off to bed with you or Father Christmas won't come.

"Do you think Father will be back?" said Rosa. "No dear" replied Alice patiently and trying very hard not to cry. "Come on, hang your stockings up." She gave them a stocking each which they put by the fireplace.

Alice warmed some water and put it in the big bowl for them to have a wash and started on Doris first. The child wasn't happy but she dutifully stood still while Alice rubbed the flannel over her face and body and put her vest on for her. Then it was Stanley's turn in the same water while Rosa helped Doris on with her nightdress. Finally, Alice tipped the water out into the yard and warmed some more up for Rosa. She was just about big enough to see to herself while Alice tucked the two younger ones into their beds and read them a story. Then it was prayers beginning with the Lord's Prayer which all three children knew by heart.

"God bless Mother and God bless Father" chanted Stanley, "and God bless Father's friend Henry and Uncle Charlie and please bring Father home."

"Amen" to that "said Alice. She tucked them both in and then went back and checked behind Rosa's ears. "all done properly young lady. Off you go then and we shall see in the morning if Father Christmas has been." She followed her into the bedroom and stood over her while the little girl also said her prayers.

"Night night Rosa" said Alice.

"Night night Mother" replied Rosa. "I shall listen out for Father Christmas's sleigh."

◆ ◆ ◆

Now was the worst time of all, when Alice was on her own. She tried to put all dreadful thoughts to the back of her mind and concentrated on tidying up and then filling the stockings. She had some little toys that had been given to her by Jessie Browne-Douglas and she had bought some crayons for Stanley and a little dolly for Doris. There was also an apple and some sweetmeats that she bought at the shops. It hadn't been easy because things were in short supply since the war. There were also some knitted dollies clothes for both Rosa and Doris and some toy soldiers for Stanley. She pushed them into each stocking and then, when she was sure the children were asleep, she crept into their bedrooms and left them on the end of the bed.

◆ ◆ ◆

It was snowing the following morning as she was awoken by the excited cries of three small children.

"Mother, Mother! Look, Father Christmas has been." All three of them came rushing into the bedroom and climbed up onto the double bed with her. "Come and see!" Rosa grabbed her arm and she all but fell over Stanley and Doris as she rushed to see.

"I have got dollies clothes and a painting book" cried Rosa.

"I got dolly, look" cried an excited little Doris. Stanley didn't know whether to play with the soldiers or stand on a chair at the window and watch the snow coming down.

Christmas had begun at Redhill. Later on, snow or no snow, they would go with their neighbours to Church and they would pray. They would pray as they had never prayed before.

CHRISTMAS DAY 1915 – THE SOMME

AS MORNING BROKE ON Christmas Day Charles would have sold his soul just to hear that 'bloody old cockerel' that got on his father's nerves so much. Instead he had woken in the trenches to a stillness. They had been issued rations and most men just sat in silence. Then suddenly there was the sound of carol singing in German, soft at first and then louder as more joined in.

"My God, it's happening again" said one of the Tommy's. This happened last year and they came out in no man's land and played football."

"See" replied Fred "they are no different to us really. They don't want to fight any more than we do."

Further up the line somebody started singing 'Good King Wenceslas' and, one by one, everyone joined in. Then suddenly one of the German soldiers emerged above the distant hill formed by the trench lines, closely followed by another. Some of our troops followed even though it had been expressly forbidden that there should be a repeat of the unauthorised truce of 1914, when famously, German and British troops defied their officers by playing football in no-mans-land.

"Come back!" yelled one of the officers, but the men ignored him and walked towards the enemy.

Charles and Fred and their friends watched as a small group of soldiers met the Germans in the middle of no-mans-land and exchanged souvenirs such as buttons and badges.

Then they shook hands and ran back to their own lines, the British getting slaps on their backs by their comrades as they all but fell back into the muddy trench. No football match this time, but they had made the gesture.

The officers were not very impressed though. They had gone against all commands and, as a result they received severe reprimands.

That was the start to their Christmas Day. They spent the rest of it intermittently singing carols and waiting for the order to stand down. It was probably the first day since Charles had arrived that there had been no casualties among the Battalion. They marched back to their base, near Berthen, where Christmas dinner had been provided by the grateful local villagers and was served by the officers. It consisted of roast goose, beef, and plum pudding plus oranges from southern France, apples and nuts. There were also cigarettes and beer.

"Well, this will do for me" said Charles.

The men were all bunched together round wooden trestle tables or sitting on the floor. If nothing else the comradeship made up for the deprivation and the hell of the mud that lay behind them, and no doubt in front of them, for there seemed to be no end to it.

"It's a jolly site better than some of that awful 'Maconochie' they give us said George. "It's made up of fatty meat and veg in gravy – yuk!"

Charles left them chatting and settled down to write to Alice and tried not to think about what may lay ahead or of what may have happened to Charlie Jones, or his friend Henry fighting in Gallipoli for that matter. It wasn't easy because he didn't want to fill a precious letter with tales of the mud and the death and the things he had seen and endured. It was the last thing she wanted to hear about.

Charles.

"Oh the world's gone mad Kate!" he wrote to Alice, "the world's gone mad".

AUTUMN 1916 - REDHILL

ALICE WALKED DOWN TO the town with three year old Doris in the push chair and Stanley and Rosa walking nicely by her side. She had letters to post. Most people, these days, had letters to post and stamps to buy. By now she recognised most of the faces and all had a tale to tell about the war and of the dreadful casualties. In fact, you couldn't miss it. There were posters everywhere and the newspapers, of course, were full of nothing else. Now there was the added threat of the zeppelins dropping bombs on London. It did not bear thinking about. Of course Stanley thought it was all very exciting. The idea of a huge balloon circling over London near to where his Grandma and Grandpa lived was exciting to a little boy who was not quite five.

She called at the Post Office to send off a parcel to Charles and a letter to her sisters. She still hadn't quite recovered from the death of her mother but kept in very close touch with all her sisters and older brother Joshua and her father Joshua Kirck.

It was a Saturday, and unusually for a Saturday, all three children had on their Sunday best clothes. Alice was taking them to the Photographer to have a special picture taken for their father. It had been Jessie that had encouraged her into getting one done.

"Alice my dear" she said "Charles must have a picture of you all to keep in his pocket."

"Oh, I don't know" Alice had replied, "I am sure it will be over soon and to have one done is almost like saying it will go on for ever."

"No, I insist Alice. Get them into their best clothes and go and see young Michael Green at the Photographers and he will do a good job for you. I shall pay for it."

Well how could she refuse? Charles had dabbled with photography since they were married, but only on a very small scale. It was something that interested him but his pictures, which he produced by using glass plates, still had many imperfections. It would be nice to have something decent done. And so it was that all three children had endured having baths the night before and the two girls had sat patiently while their mother did their hair up in rags to make curls.

"I want you to look your very best because we are going to have our picture taken for your father tomorrow" said Alice when Rosa complained.

"It's not fair!" exclaimed Rosa. "I am always last to go in the bath and I end up with all their dirty water."

"Well you are the biggest" replied Alice patiently "and they don't make much mess." She turned to Stanley. "Stanley! You make sure you go out the back to the lavvy before you get in the bath. Rosa does not want your wee in it."

This was where Alice missed having a man about the house. The tin bath full of water was heavy and to pull it out of the house and empty it outside called for a great deal of strength, especially when it has to be done three times. Therefore Alice did the same as most families. The youngest had the bath first and, provided the water wasn't too bad, it was topped up with warm water from the kettle on the range and then the next one got in. By the time it got to Rosa it was a hard job to pull the overflowing bath outside.

Now, with the girls having endured the rags in their hair, they were on their way to the professional photographer in Brighton Road.

She pushed open the door and the bell rang as she ushered the children into the shop. Michael Green was there waiting for them.

"What lovely children Mrs. Ratcliff" he said "Come with me and we will take a really nice picture of you all."

Stanley thought it was all very interesting but not as good as playing with his toy car on the kitchen floor. Doris wasn't sure about any of it. She wasn't sure about this strange man with the camera on the long sticks and being ushered and positioned on a chair.

However, all three children did as they were told.

"Now you be good children and do what the man says" said Alice "and then, when we go to the shops I shall buy you some sweets."

"Father has been gone a very long time" said Rosa "I think it is about time he came home to us."

"He has gone to war" Stanley informed her patiently. He was always telling her that he had gone to war but she never took any notice of him. In any case his eye was on Mr. Green who was pointing the funny looking camera at them and he kept disappearing under a cloth.

"Peep po" he said as he came back out from underneath. He went up to them and adjusted a position here and there and they watched, not quite knowing what to expect next.

"That's it Rosa, you keep an eye on Doris" he said. Then he ran back to his camera, satisfied with his handiwork. He covered his head up again and there was a flash and a small bang which made the children jump.

"All done" he said "I will have that ready for you on Monday Mrs. Ratcliff.

"Thank you Mr. Green." She put Doris in the push chair and ushered the children out of the shop.

She had made them a promise of some sweets so they would go and see if they could find some humbugs. That should keep them quiet, though she made a mental note to make sure they scrubbed their teeth properly. There was a chill in the air as they walked to the shops and the trees were starting to get a tinge of red to them. Alice shuddered at the idea of the Germans taking over the whole of Europe for that is what it looked as though they wanted to do. She knew that men were dying in the trenches by the thousands in their efforts to keep the Germans from taking over France and then, no doubt, Britain. That had been made clear by the continued use of zeppelins over London. Nowhere seemed to be safe any more. Also, the roads were packed with vehicles carrying soldiers back and forth to the station or to hospitals which were being set up all over the place. It felt like bedlam and she was glad to get into the Church Hall and mix with a group of other ladies who had small children. They were a Club that had grown over the past few months and all had one thing in common, one loved-one or more fighting in the War. They all sat in a circle and knitted socks and mittens for the soldiers while the children played.

"Hello Alice" they all called "Look at you! Don't you all look smart today children."

"Hello Annie, Ivy, hello Winifred!" she spoke to each one of the dozen or so ladies. "Have you heard any more from your husband yet Phyllis?"

"No I haven't!" Phyllis started to dissolve into tears and Alice immediately realised it was the wrong thing to ask. She thought of her brother and Charles and she felt like joining her. It was a hard job keeping a stiff upper lip these days.

"I saw a film at the cinema the other day" said Winifred "it showed the men in the trenches and it looked so awful. Of course you couldn't hear anything and the chap playing the piano wasn't very good but it was marvellous to see it."

That was definitely the wrong thing to say and so Annie and Daisy tried to change the subject and get peoples minds focussed on playing 'Oranges and Lemons' with the children.

"I read in the paper that a group of women in Anglesey in Wales have started a Women's Institute" said Annie. "They make cakes and jam and send it to the soldiers."

"Maybe we could do that" said Alice. "It sounds like a good idea to me."

They chatted on and then Alice decided that it was time to go back home so that Doris could have her afternoon nap. Life in Redhill had to go on as normally as possible. It had been enough excitement for one day. First of all there was the photograph, then the bull's eyes and then a play with the other children. But really, what they really needed, what everyone needed, was the man of the house back. Alice thought it was just as well she hadn't seen the film of the men in the trenches that Winifred had seen. "Sometimes" thought Alice "ignorance can be bliss!"

She was pleased with the end result of the effort to get the photograph done and enclosed it in her next letter to Charles. Whether he would receive it was another matter but at least she tried. The postal service was pretty good and the French did their best to make sure the post got to the Army and eventually to the front line, but it was inevitable that some would go astray. She was also given a copy and this she put in a silver frame and put on the mantelpiece.

She tried to keep up with letter writing as much as possible. She kept in constant touch with her sisters and her father Joshua Kirck and also with her older brother Joshua. Since the death of Sarah, Joshua and his two remaining unmarried daughters and, also of course Charlie, moved to East Sheen where he still continued his duties as a Church Lay Reader. Everyone was worried that there had been no news from young Charlie though. Then, one never to be forgotten day in November, not long after they had their professional picture taken, Alice received news in the form of a telegram. It was from her Father. That, in itself, filled her with foreboding straight away. Her father did not normally do the writing. He left that to his daughters, and even if he did, it would just be an ordinary letter and not a telegram. It couldn't be about Charles because, of course, the Army would contact her. No, she didn't need to look any further. This was going to be about Charlie. Only Doris was in the house when the telegram arrived. Stanley had just started school so both he and Rosa were at lessons.

Dear Alice, Joshua Kirck wrote. *We have just received news that your beloved brother Charlie was killed on 20th October fighting for his country.*

She sank to her knees in despair and Doris watched as her mother wept. All Alice could do was to write back to her father. There wasn't even a funeral to go to.

A few weeks later an officer from the London Regiment paid a visit to Joshua Kirck to give his condolences. It seemed that Charlie had been very brave and had crept right up to the enemy lines in the dark in order to listen to their conversations and learn what their plans were. He was able to interpret and

The studio photograph.

transmit the information back to his commanders. Then he went back for a second time and was able to impart further information before getting shot and killed. In so doing he had probably saved many lives. It had already been recommended that he get the Distinguished Conduct Medal.

The news, whilst filling Alice with pride, did nothing to relieve her despair. But she was not alone and as the new Women's Institute was being formed there was hardly a person she knew who did not know of someone who had died or had been terribly wounded.

It was a year since Charles had left. She knew, of course, that for most of the younger ones it had been two years. What nobody knew was how many more.

◆ ◆ ◆

IT WAS APPROACHING THE second Christmas without her husband when Alice received a letter from Manchester. It was addressed to Charles but she opened it. It wasn't something that she would normally do, but she didn't know where he was or whether this letter was urgent. It was from Daisy, the wife of his friend Henry who he had started out with at Althorp House, all those years ago, when he was just seventeen.

Frederick Charles Jones.

"I thought you might like to know" she wrote "that Henry is still alive but he has been taken a prisoner of war and he is in the hands of the Turks. Alice gasped. "The Turks!" she said out loud. "From what I can make out it is pretty awful but he had to go into hospital and was given some pencil and paper to write home."

"Oh good grief" thought Alice "the whole world is going up in flames".

AUTUMN 1916 – THE SOMME

CHARLES SAT ON A camp bed in the tented accommodation which had been provided back from the front line, where the soldiers rested between advances. It seemed to be days of boredom and hanging around followed by a couple of days of concentrated hell in the mud of the trenches at every attempt to move forward for a few inches. The Germans were being held back but it was at great cost. He had just received a parcel from Alice and opened it to find the photograph that she had taken by Michael Green. He sat and looked at it for ages and then passed it round for the small group of soldiers who were resting with him to see.

"What smashing children and such a lovely wife!" remarked Bob, a little chap who didn't look old enough to be in the Army.

"Great Charles" said Fred. "Something worth fighting for eh?"

Charles put the photo carefully in his top pocket and read Alice's letter. She told him about the death of Charlie and also about the letter she had received from Daisy. He punched his fist in the air and then threw his tin hat across the floor.

"Damn it!" he shouted "is there no end to it, Charlie was only twenty-five, and God alone knows what is happening to my friend Henry."

But life and death went on in the trenches and day after day the men endured the relentless battles and a life living on preserved meat and biscuits.

◆ ◆ ◆

WITH THE REST PERIOD finished it was back 'up the tree' again, or sending signals from within the trench. By now he was used to seeing the brave 'wirers' fixing up barbed wire and stakes to protect the trenches as far as possible, or watching the Lewis Guns firing at the enemy, or the skies lit up with flares. More and more there was the use of aeroplanes and he watched fascinated as they circled around the sky and then, like his comrades he would dive for cover as they tried to shoot each other or the troops on the ground below. He watched as two aeroplanes collided with each other and came crashing to the ground. He also thought of Henry and wondered what was happening to him.

"Gawd help him if he is in the hands of the Turks" Bob had said. "I heard that they show no mercy."

Now it was quiet again. The guns had stopped as both British and Germans regrouped and went back to receive further instructions from their respective Commanders. Charles had time to sit in his Observation post and survey the land. It was a horrifying sight to the man who knew nothing else but making beauty with his flowers or growing vegetables. All he could see was mud pockmarked with shell holes and stretcher bearers running out to bring back the wounded while the dead lay in bits where they fell.

"What a waste!" he exclaimed to anyone who happened to be listening. "What a bloody waste."

1916 Somewhere in Turkey

THE YEAR BEFORE CHARLES arrived in Northern France, his friend Henry was in the advance on Achi Baba on the Gallipoli Peninsula. It was a crucial objective in the struggle against the Ottoman Empire and its German allies. He was, however, taken Prisoner-of-War and, just as Bob said "the Turks showed no mercy." Their idea of 'getting rid' of their prisoners was to take them on forced marches across the desert until, one by one, they dropped to the ground and died. Whether it was because of his fitness in having been a gardener all his life, or just because of sheer true grit, Henry was one of the few left standing and he, along with some Australians, ended up in a camp somewhere in Turkey. He was at death's door but realised how lucky he was when one of the men whispered to him,

"This is a bit of luck my friend. Much more of that and we would have been a gonna."

At this point in time Henry did not really care but he was vaguely aware of being left on a mattress.

It turned out that they were at a camp called Hadjekerri and that most of the prisoners were of the 1st Worcestershire Regiment. The first job they were given was on the railroad and they had to work filling trucks with sand and stones. They were overseen by a Turk carrying a D'jack, which was a sort of whip. Many of the men got to the point where they could not even lift a shovel. Henry stopped for a rest but didn't realise that the Turk was so near and saw him. He dealt him a blow behind his neck with the whip. Henry could not stop himself and tried to hit him but instead, being weak, he fell forward only to receive a second blow in the face.

"You swine" he cried.

Again he was struck and for many days could barely open his eyes with the pain.

"Let him come down here again pard and I will lump him under the chin and pretty quick" said an Australian by the name of Steele. "I have been watching him for a few days now. You go over there to where they are breaking the rocks and stones – go on" he remarked "do as I tell you before he comes down."

"Thanks chum but be careful", said Henry, "you don't want to cause trouble."

"I'll trouble the bastard if he lifts that whip to me," said Andrew Steele.

They spent their days breaking up rocks and stones for the railroads and their nights lying wherever they could in the camp and trying to evade the torture of their captors. They would whip a person on their backside and on the soles of their feet so that they could neither sit nor stand. It was like a permanent nightmare.

◆ ◆ ◆

THE WEEKS AND MONTHS of captivity turned into years but eventually all the prisoners were given pencil and paper so they could write home. Whether their letters ever got home was another matter. Despite the awful circumstances the men became comrades and all looked out for each other.

"Nobody is going to believe what we are going through out here" said a Lance Corporal called Taylor. "There is nobody here to tell our story and what we have been through"

"I think we should try and keep diaries" said Andrew Steele so that people, one day, will know what these bastards were like."

Henry knew that many of the men did keep diaries when they were in the trenches before they were captured, but many got lost, especially on the forced marches. It was nothing for the Turks to strip a person completely of their clothes and just leave them naked in the desert. Now, however, it was different. Now, the Germans had taken over and they were in a proper Prisoner-of-War camp.

"I never thought I would hear myself say that I was glad to be in the hands of the Germans" said Henry.

Things were strict but the Turks, who were under the control of the Germans couldn't get away with quite as much as they did in the previous years of captivity. The prisoners actually found themselves with time on their hands.

"You are right" said Henry "we owe it to our children."

The following day he went to the Commander of the allied prisoners, who was of the 1st Worcestershire Regiment, and asked if it was possible to get hold of an exercise book. Within a few days one appeared.

"Here you are old chap, but I would not let the enemy see it if I were you."

Whenever Henry had a spare moment he started writing. Growing flowers and vegetables and watching out for the 'Red Earl' at Althorp House, when they were barely teenagers, seemed like a different world away.

"This is for my wife and my children" he wrote, "It is my story and if you don't believe it then don't bother reading it because it is not for you."

THE ADVANCE ON ACHI BABA by Henry Winters

7th day of August 1915

The big advance was ordered right along the line right from end to end of the peninsular. We were to attack Achi Baba – a fortified hill on our front. This attack was on a huge scale for every man from end to end had to swarm towards our enemy. It was this way:-

The flanks were to make the attack first, after half an hour the front had to proceed – thus the numerous amount of troops that were in the conflict, This Sunday morning was bright and far along the line you could see the men preparing.

I sat there and waited and wondered if I would escape death again.. It was a sight never to be forgotten – I thought of home – always of the ones I love and of Daisy. What far off glance was in the eye! What tender memories fell to mind – a sorrowful heart beating, perhaps to cease for ever. One of the chaps made up this poem while we were waiting.

"Some Mother will lose her son before the morrow morning,
Some lass will lose her lad before the day is dawning.
It may be me, it may be you,
The charge will be remembered for years
The charge was made at the Dardanelles
By the Lancashire Fusiliers."

After a day or two in this position we began to prepare for a further move that found us nearer to our objective, a fortified hill named 'Archie Bar'. We worked like stink to get in touch with our comrades in the rear – we were successful in capturing a trench – the first thing a party is told to do is to commence digging a communication trench to the trench we had left and also they dig to meet us (to be all together). This accomplished, we settled down again for a spell, only to be attacked by our enemy – numerous conflicts and counter attacks together with severe fighting lasting all that day found us returning back to the old formation from where we started at first. The aim and the desire on this ordered retirement was to hold on to the last trench and remain here at all costs – our heavy artillery and rapid fire checked the Turks from a further onslaught of us. However, no more attacks on our enemy's front were ordered, for the time being anyway.

WOUNDED AND TAKEN PRISONER

A sound as if the skies above had opened - suddenly the pattering noise increased with tenfold violence. The alarm sounded – here they are! Rapid fire! Hang on to the trench at all cost was the order sent down. The guns barked from both sides – the shells falling short or well forward – our heavy fire took effect. At first we thought they would go back but no (not this time).

On – on they came – a sight I will never forget – we could see nothing but Turks left and right of us – crowds of them – they came at us arm in arm as if there was no firing. The excitement was intense – beads of perspiration on my forehead – our foe galloping on in one great effort to sweep us off the face of the earth. They were in among us – we were fighting like grim death (some of the lads retired). I did not hear any order to retire, if such was ordered, but like a fool I remained.

I should have made the same hurried exit. I was rooted there – glued to the spot – where were my senses? I stood there as if I was fastened down they were in on us so suddenly. All I remember seeing was faces – such faces – faces of hatred.

My fight for exit never came – I saw a Turk on the parapet in front of me and then I felt a sharp piercing sensation – a burning feeling at the back of my left shoulder. I knew I had got the bayonet. I pushed out my rifle to defend myself but it fell out of my grasp. I distinctly felt the thrust and the drawing out. (This drawing out sensation revived or woke me so I moved quickly and sudden) then shrivelled up and fell flat on my face.

To save myself — to avoid a second attempt I did not completely faint away — only slightly — enough to remember what I had done — for by doing this was the best possible way — being alone — it being madness to fight again and odds handicapped me as it was and I could not defend myself.

Here I lay not daring to move a hair — to do so would have meant certain death. I lay there fully conscious of what was going on. Any moment I may be turned over and finished — what agony I endured! What a test for my brain! The throb of my wound was like the ticking of a clock — my brain was working rapidly — thoughts of every description flashed through my mind — I was in a tight place — however an inward feeling stayed me in this pose. Perhaps when it is dark I can get back — perhaps our lads will make a charge on them.

Oh the agony of waiting — what to do for the best. Oh Daisy, how long I lay there I am at a loss to account for then I suddenly felt a quantity of earth falling upon me — was I going mad — had my brain snapped under the strain — was this the thought of one dying. This earth was beginning to get very heavy — then it dawned on me for this is one way to bury the dead for pulling the sides in on the bodies. Oh no — I would not be buried alive — I would sooner die sudden.

OUT OF THE JAWS OF DEATH

On feeling this heavy burden, come what may, I got up, weak from the loss of blood. All around me appearing in a whirl — I felt myself sinking. I saw dozens of bayonets pointed towards my chest. I shut my eyes awaiting my end. I had given up all hopes and thought I was done for but then a Sergeant approached and saved me or I would not have lived to write this diary. This Sergeant spoke fairly good English as he said "English get up."

I stood alone in the mob – a mob of wild animals as it was – men who do not know what life is. However, the men obeyed and fell back at this Sergeant's command. He also instructed two soldiers to take me up the Trench – to a safe spot I expect. I could perceive by the tone of his voice that he had little hopes of me getting there for I had to journey in the midst of them and also I felt as though there was just one false step between me and death.

My heart was heavy within me but at that moment my thoughts turned to my beloved wife and children.

The end of the trench was now very near. We three journeyed on until we reached a bend – then quite unexpected a Turk came forward and dealt me a tremendous blow on my jaw which counted me out (for the first time in my life). I remember seeing him come forward but had no idea that he was coming towards me – then I remember falling in a heap, then being dragged a distance. The next instance again falling with a thud – then I became insensible. On recovering from my faint I found myself close to a parapet looking up into the face of my own countrymen captured as myself.

There is a strange and peculiar sensation experienced on recovering from fainting – a half waking, half sleeping condition with a feeling of weariness. At first as I slowly recovered and heard the voices of my comrades I thought I was going mad, but very soon understood and slowly opened my eyes to meet my mates. I now raised myself the best I could and found that my company consisted of three lads of my own regiment. I smiled under difficulties and looked up saying "blimey what a show – we are in a fix now – roll on the end."

The prisoners were moved from place to place and it wasn't long before Henry and his friends found themselves, once again, on the march. This time to a place called Serjihan. He carefully stored his precious exercise book in the lining of his hat. It was a short march this time though, of about ten miles. He continued here with his diary.

"As time went on a supply of clothing was sent to our camp, the indent having been sent away to a Corporal Poory, an Indian officer who was in charge of the stores, Clothes were sent and stored from the Americans for prisoners. Myself and my friend Robert Ward were not included in this indent because we were last to come to the camp, but a note was sent including us afterwards.

Ward slipped off from work for his issue and got it. Anyone can proceed to the village on application for sentries are going there regularly. Men were in the habit of going in parties of four or more – so it got a somewhat general thing. Nobody said anything, nobody stopped us. As I said, Ward silently took off and returned the proud possessor of a full rig out – boots, socks, shirt, underpants, suit, overcoat, towel, soap etc. He said to me "there you go Henry, Why don't you take off for yours?"

"OK" I replied, so after our work breaking stones I journeyed over to the sentries hut and asked if I could go. He pointed to a wagon on the railway line which was about to proceed there and instructed me to go on that and come back with the others. I took this opportunity quickly. I asked Ward to look after my diary though and, as it turned out, it was a good job I did.

ROBBED BY ARABS

On arrival at the stores I was unable to be supplied until the Captain was present. He was out at the time. I waited about two hours and then I duly received and signed for my kit. I made tracks for my return journey to camp by foot (of course the wagon had gone back).

I knew perfectly well that I was undergoing a great risk for not only are you in danger of being accosted but also could look as though you were trying to escape.

I made for cover — to do so was best, but when I turned off towards the line I was accosted by a group of Arabs. I was roughly handled. One got hold of me in his cunning way and with his knife he motioned to me to sit down, the others snatching my bag. I lashed out as my strength would allow but it was of no use — I was in for it. They made me strip — this done I sat down again. The Arab stood over me and remarked "you get plenty of clothes — I want."

Here I sat naked as a new born babe. I kept shouting at the top of my voice "Sentry, sentry come here Arab kill"

They took off and left me.. My cry for assistance was of little use them being so far away but I only cried out on chance that someone would hear me. They took everything off me, I was powerless. Anyway I returned with nothing and had to make the best of it.

I reported but the German Commander only grunted as much as to say 'it is your own fault'. Anyway he gave me clothes and a pair of Dutch clogs. I was broke, down and out and had to start over again. 'Once bitten twice shy' was my motto hereafter.

"I am writing this so that, if I am killed," he wrote, "somebody may find it, and one day people will know what happened here in this forgotten place on the other side of the world."

CHAPTER X

The Beginning of the End

REDHILL 1918

IT WAS A BEAUTIFUL spring day and everyone had just finished celebrating Easter. Alice took the children to church and everyone had some daffodils to bring home. Rosa still went to the gate every so often and just stood there to see if she could spot her father coming down the road, but gradually she started to give up.

"Come on dear" called Alice for, what seemed like the millionth time since he left. "Come and play." Rosa was nearly eight now and it was remarkable how fast they had all grown. Charles would certainly see a difference in them when he came home. Alice flatly refused to contemplate any idea that he would not come home even though she had heard very little from him in the past few months, but lots in the newspapers about how the Germans were advancing and that the British and French were struggling to keep them back, and always, always, reports of the casualties. Many of the big houses of the type that Alice had worked in since she was fourteen had now been given over to hospitals and women all over the country were volunteering to act as nurses.

The Women's Institute had gone from strength to strength in the village and it had been Alice's salvation to have the company of other ladies together with doing something constructive for the soldiers fighting in the trenches. Mrs.

Browne-Douglas had also joined and they all met every week at the Church Hall or in one of the rooms in Hillbrow.

Now Alice had finished for the day and it was time to get the children in, bathed and ready for bed. She thought of all of the other children all over the country who waited and waited for their fathers to come home and no means of knowing what was happening other than what was in the newspapers.

Rosa reluctantly pulled herself away from the gate and followed her brother and sister into the house, just as her mother's friend Phyllis from the W.I. came running up the road brandishing a newspaper.

"Alice, Alice, have you seen this." She was gasping for breath. "The Americans have entered the war. Now it will end with the help of them."

This was, indeed, good news.

Alice grabbed the paper from her friend. The Americans, who had tried to stay neutral all this time, were now entering the war. It could not go on much longer. Also Russia was exiting from all hostilities.

"It says here that Field Marshal Paul Von Hindenberg and General Erich Lundendorff told Kaiser Wilhelm II that the War was lost and that negotiations for an Armistice should proceed at once." She waved the paper in the air. "This is the beginning of the end Alice."

Alice just hoped she was right.

"Come in Phyllis and we'll have a cup of tea" she said "I think I can find us some cakes."

Phyllis followed her into the house and she played with the children while Alice put the kettle on the kitchen range and boiled it up for tea.

"I honestly can not think of anyone who has not lost a loved one" said Phyllis "it is just awful, and they all thought they were going off on such adventures. They didn't have a clue."

"Well I am not sure about that Phyllis. I know you are right with all those that went off in nineteen fourteen. I think they thought it was a huge lark and a chance to see the world, but I don't think Charles was under any illusions. He had an idea of what he was going into. He followed it daily in the newspapers."

"I think that makes it worse somehow" said Phyllis. "To know what you are going into. Oh dear, what a mess. Do you think us women could run the world a little bit better Alice?"

"Well Mrs. Pankhurst thinks so!" she laughed. She poured out the tea into the pot and let it stew for a minute and then poured it out. "She is right though. It is outrageous that women do not have the vote." She passed the cakes to the children and gave them a glass of milk each.

"What's 'a vote?" said Stanley.

"It's when you choose who is best to do something" replied Phyllis "and looking at that crayoning that you have just done, I think you are the best just at the moment."

Stanley went off happy and the chat ended in laughter.

"But still" mused Alice as Phyllis put her hat on and she showed her to the door, "the idea that he has been gone two and a half years now is just unbelievable."

Charles and Jessie Browne-Douglas bought all the newspapers they could and Alice got the chance to keep up with everything that was being reported. Mr. Brown-Douglas spent much of his time in London but he also oversaw the upkeep of the property. It was clearly too big for them though and he was always talking about selling up.

"All these big houses are going now Jessie," he said as Alice was putting Doris's coat on and getting ready to leave. "It's going to be an entirely different world for that little one I fancy," he said to no-one in particular. Nobody was going to argue with him. He turned the page and then burst into huge guffaws of laughter.

"It says here that the German Navy have gone on strike! I bet that didn't go down well with the Kaiser."

It was music to Alice's ears. Maybe this war would soon be over after all.

He threw the paper down on the table.

"What we need is a wireless" he said "they have experimented with it in America, or so it says here, and we are only a short way away from getting the wireless. At least if we had one of those we could hear more of what is going on."

Neither Alice nor Jessie could cope with the idea of having a wireless in your own home. True, you could go to the cinema in some towns and you could see a silent film. People were just starting to get used to the idea of that, but a wireless in your own home? It didn't seem possible. *"But then"* thought Alice as she put the 'dust sucker' away *"a few years ago nobody thought we would have one of these either, nor the electricity with which to power it."* Not that Alice had electricity, although her sisters in Barnes had it now. Yes, there were a lot of changes and Charles would find things very different when he came home, and he would come home. She would not let her mind think anything different.

"Come on Doris, or we will have your brother and sister home before we are. Maybe we shall get a letter from Father today."

JULY 1918 - NR YPRES

CHARLES WAS WITH HIS Battalion on the outskirts of Ypres. The sun was shining but it didn't alter the mud that surrounded them. For nearly three years he felt he had lived like a zombie and there was still no end to it. He had alternated between being 'up a tree' as he called the observation post, to 'down in a ditch' and he still hadn't quite decided which was worse. Fred had long since been killed and carried off to 'who knows where' and now he was surrounded by others, many of whom he had never seen before. The trenches had been expanded and fortified and the whole area was a series of underground tunnels which had been reinforced by the engineers. On the other side of 'no-man's land' the enemy had done the same and so you could walk along the vast warren of passages and almost be within touching distance and yet below ground.

"I feel more like a bloody mole than ever" said Charles as he and his partner ran along the trench to take up a new position. "I think I preferred it up the tree."

The Battalion had just finished a brief respite back behind the lines where they had been fed and watered and had a chance to get clean clothes and bathe. He tried to write home to Alice and to his parents but it was difficult. What could anyone say? Unlike Henry, he did not want to relive it all by writing about it, nor did he want to worry them with tales of being surrounded by dead bodies and the constant shelling. He could hardly talk about the weather or about birds singing. There were no birds except for the pigeons kept for sending messages. He didn't even know if his letter would reach them, but he wrote a few lines in pencil.

Over the summer the Germans had got the upper hand but now they were being pushed back. Moreover, the news that the American's had entered the war boosted everybody's confidence. It wasn't over yet though. Not by any means.

"Well at least we will all be clean and shaved if we get blown up" said Bob Baxter as they formed up ready for another stint 'up the tree'. He was a young chap who had just been assigned to share the signalling duties with Charles in place of Fred. Charles didn't think he even looked old enough to shave.

They climbed up the ladders to the observation platform from where they and their officers had a good view of the battlefield. Unbeknown to them the Allies were winning the war.

All along the trenches there were frightened men in their hundreds and thousands waiting for the order to go 'over the top'.

"It's these I feel sorry for" Bob whispered "they have to go first. At least we don't have to go first."

"It's those bloody 'whizz-bangs' that I don't like" grunted Charles. He could see wounded men lying on the ground waiting for stretcher bearers and the trenches were a heaving mass of humanity in the mud. Mud that stretched for miles in all directions, littered with bits of body and water filled craters. Bob peered through his binoculars at the observation post way in the distance.

"It's the order to go" he said simply.

456 Tanks attacked the German Army east of Amiens Charles found out later that thirteen thousand prisoners were taken during the advance. A couple of weeks later nearly one thousand five hundred aircraft took part in an allied co-ordinated air and ground attack. But he saw none of that. The war for him was over as suddenly as it had started.

The men scrambled down the ladders but as they did so there was a flash, bang and a huge explosion of dirt and debris from the dug out as a mortar landed just yards away. Some men were killed outright and there were the screams of others while thousands more stormed ahead. Charles knew no more and, by the side of him, among others, young Bob Baxter lay dead.

◆ ◆ ◆

CHARLES LAY ON HIS back and gazed at the roof of the hospital tent. He vaguely remembered being man handled onto a stretcher and then the excruciating pain which seemed to be all over his body, bright lights flashing through his head, and then, as the blood flowed, he was unconscious again. When he came round his head seemed to be swathed in cloth.

"Come on old fella', wake up!" It was a Medical Officer "You are not dead yet but your war is over." There were more bright lights and then everything went black again. The next time he woke up he could feel the movement of a ship and smell the stink of wounded and dying men on their way back home. His head was covered in bandages and he couldn't walk.

CHAPTER XI

Chailey Green, 1915

Alice had been busy showing Doris how to make pastry when the postman called with a letter from her sister Laney. In it was a newspaper cutting from their paper giving an account of the death of her brother Charlie. The tears rolled down her face as she read it. She wiped her cheeks with floury hands while Doris looked on. She would be going to school soon and this was a special treat. She didn't like it being interrupted.

"Come on Mother" she called "help me roll the pastry. Why are you sad?"

"You roll it nicely Doris" she answered. "We shall have some nice biscuits for when Rosa and Stanley get home from school." She turned back to Laney's letter.

"We are all keeping well and isn't it good news that the war may be ending. I thought you would like this newspaper article about our Charlie. It's taken a while since his death, but we are so proud of him as he has been awarded the DCM..."

"Hmm" granted Alice, "Fat lot of good that is without the person to wear it." For all that though she was proud but it was with a mixture of pride, anger and overwhelming sadness that she read the newspaper article. She's had some time now to get used to his death but this was bringing it all back.

"DCM FOR BARNES HERO" It read. "The many friends of the late Sgt. F.C. Jones, of the London Regiment, who fell fighting for his country, will be glad to know that his father,

Mr. J.K. Jones of 16 Stanley Road, East Sheen, is the proud recipient of the Distinguished Conduct Medal in recognition of his son's services to his country. Born in Archway Street, Barnes, twenty-five years ago, the deceased, as a boy was in the choir of the Parish Church. He was a scholar at the Latymer School, Hammersmith, where he was very popular with his personifications of Henry Lauder.

The official notification of the Award read:

For conspicuous gallantry in action... he carried out a daring reconnaissance with great skill and discovered valuable information.

"Well it is a good job that Mother is not here to endure this," she said out loud. It was a bitter sweet award. Of course they would all be proud, but no medal would bring him back. "Twenty-five!" she sighed. "Just twenty-five years old. What a waste."

"Mother!" the impatient voice of Doris brought her back to reality and she put away Laney's letter. There was a nice picture of Charlie in the newspaper and she would cut it out and keep it for ever. All she wanted now was news of Charles. There had been no word of him or his Regiment for ages. Letters were very few and far between, written in pencil and telling her nothing. She got most of her knowledge from the newspapers or the gossip at the Women's Institute.

She got back to helping the little girl with her pastries. By now Doris had covered herself in flour and there would be a mess to clear up. Unlike Jessie Brown-Douglas, Alice did not have a dust sucker or whatever it was called.

She had just managed to get her cleaned up when the peace was shattered by Rosa and Stanley coming up the path. One day they would understand how brave their Uncle 'Charlie' had been, but they were too young just now.

"I saw an aeroplane go over our school" said Stanley. "It had big wings and made a lot of noise."

"Go and get your play clothes on children and then you can have some of Doris's biscuits and you can tell me all about the aeroplane Stanley."

She gave them their milk and biscuits and wondered for the umpteenth time when Charles would be home. There was so much talk about this awful war coming to an end.

◆ ◆ ◆

IT WAS OCTOBER AND the leaves were turning orange, and there was a chill in the air, when there was an unexpected knock on the door.

"Goodness me, who can that be at this time of day?" she said as she patted down her hair and brushed down her dress. "I'm not expecting anybody." She was just getting ready to get the children some soup. Her heart sank to her feet when she saw the telegraph boy.

"Oh no!" she gasped. She took the telegram and didn't know whether to laugh or cry at the news telling her that her husband had been severely wounded and had been admitted to hospital at Chailey, near Hayward's Heath. He was home, but wounded! How wounded? There was talk of men with limbs blown off, poisoned by gas, blinded, burnt... how wounded? Then she looked at the telegram again. "*No longer physically fit for war service. Admitted to Beechland Hospital, Chailey. Nr. Hayward's Heath.*" She had tears rolling down her face but she suddenly burst out laughing, much to the surprise of the telegraph boy. "Chailey! That's near to where all three of my children were born. Why would they send him back there?"

"Maybe it is the only place available" volunteered the lad. "There are a lot of wounded soldiers missus."

He was right - of course he was right. There were hundreds of thousands of them. Maybe the Army thought that we still lived there. Maybe there has been a mix up. She didn't know. Frankly, she didn't care. He was back and she would have to make arrangements to visit him. The children looked on, fascinated by their mother's outburst. Only Rosa realised the true meaning of it.

"Does this mean that my Father is home?" she said.

"I believe it does" said Alice, "but he has been wounded and he is not very well so we have to wait until he gets better."

"I was only a little girl when he left but I am a big girl now" she replied "I can help look after him."

"I am sure you can Rosa" smiled Alice. "We will all look after him, but first I have to go and visit and you shall have to stay with my friend Phyllis while I do so.

"I want to go too" said Rosa.

"Not this time darling" replied her mother. "I don't know how he will be. I shall go this time and then I will take you once I find out how he is. You will be helping me if you be a good girl and have your soup."

Suitably re-assured Rosa had her soup and then went off to read her brother and sister a story. The first thing Alice had to do was write a quick letter to Charles's parents. The following day she would post it and she would see Mrs. Browne-Douglas.

"Fancy him being at Chailey" she thought. *"Of all places"*. It was only a short journey on the bus from where they had lived at Butlers Green Road.

◆ ◆ ◆

ALICE WALKED UP THE lane towards the large Beechlands House, near Chailey. To most people it would have been daunting to say the least but this very large country house was small compared to some of the places she had worked in during

Charles at Beechlands (3ʳᵈ row, arrowed).

the years and she also knew the area well. She had caught the train and bus and now it was a short step up the tree lined road that lead gently past the farmlands and rolling countryside. The very idea of Germans bringing their tanks and aeroplanes over this country was unthinkable.

She had spoken to Mrs. Browne-Douglas who had been more than happy to give her the time off and Phyllis was looking after the children. Now, all she had to do was find her husband. She had found out that there were just forty men convalescing here at Beechlands. Originally the Voluntary Aid Detachment had occupied Hickwells which was just up the road and was originally a Workhouse. But just recently some of the patients had been moved here, to the home of Mrs. Harcourt-Rose.

"Hmm, clearly a very wealthy woman!" thought Alice.

She walked down the drive and passed some men strolling in the grounds. Some with heads bandaged and some with a limb missing or being lead around by caring nurses. All were wearing the uniform of the convalescent soldier which was blue with a white collar. She smiled at them but could see no sign of Charles. She was greeted at the door by a young nurse.

"Can I help you?" she asked.

"Yes please" said Alice tentatively. "I believe Mr. Charles Ratcliff is here. I am his wife and I have come to see him.

"Come in and follow me" said the little nurse. "Mr. Ratcliff can't walk just yet but you can see him. He is in the ward."

Alice followed her into what, she guessed, was once the ballroom of this great house. There were the beds lined up, each one giving rest to a badly wounded and heavily bandaged man. It was hard to pick anyone out and many looked like they were fighting for life. It took her a while to recognize him but at the far end, his leg up in a hoist and his head covered in bandages, was Charles. She ran down the room and fell to her knees at the side of the bed. He slowly opened his eyes.

"Hang on Kate" he whispered "watch the leg!"

Once again her hand was in his strong brown hand and once again she could look into his grey/blue eyes.

"Thank God you are alive" she cried, "thank God my prayers have been answered!"

"I think I got a bit of a knock on the head" he said "shrapnel. I might be here for some while."

"I'll bring Rosa with me next time" she said. "She wanted to come this time but I did not know what to expect." She looked around at the other men lying in the ward in various stages of recovery. It was an awesome sight and she still wondered whether it was right for a little girl to see. There were some who had clearly been burnt and others who had arms and legs strapped up, while others, like Charles, had bandaged heads. The term 'wounded soldiers' never had a truer meaning. She vowed she would never use the phrase again when Stanley fell over and hurt his knee.

"Maybe I will be up and about next time" said Charles "I can hop!" He laughed wryly.

"I expect you will get one of those fancy uniforms with the white collars" Alice replied. It was a job to think of something to say and the tears kept flowing.

"I have written to your father and mother" she said "I have told them that you are back safe and sound."

"Well safe Kate" said Charles, "not so sure about sound. But what news?

"As I told you in my letter, my brother Charlie did not come back." She filled up with tears again.

"I know, damn it!" roared Charles. If he could have done he would have slung something across the room. "Such a waste, such a waste. It is all a waste Kate."

"He got the DCM"

"Hang the DCM! That won't bring him back."

"I have written to your friend Henry's wife" she went on. "She hasn't heard anything more of him."

He sank back onto his pillow and she could see the tragic news was getting all too much for him. It was time to talk about other things, like flowers and how the children were doing at school. After a while she could see he was in pain and it wasn't long before the nurses turned up to make him as comfortable as possible.

"At least I know you are being looked after now" said Alice "and I will bring Rosa to see you next time."

She kissed him goodbye and stayed while he dozed off. She saw the Matron on the way out.

"Hello" said the efficient looking woman "my name is Emily Morris-Marshall. Don't worry, Mrs. Ratcliff. He is safe in our hands." Alice surveyed the rather large smart woman with greying hair and believed he would.

"He received a large chunk of shrapnel to the head and leg" she went on, "but we have been able to remove it. It's all a question of waiting for the wounds to heal." She took Alice's arm. "Trust us" she smiled. "I think he will still keep his brains."

Alice walked down the path to the entrance passing other people on their way in to see loved ones. They nodded and passed the time of day.

"Well at least we are not visiting a mortuary" said one lady as she passed her "so many are."

She went off home happier than she had been in nearly four years. There was a real possibility that the war was going to end soon and maybe then things would get back to some sort of normality, although everybody knew that the world would never be the same again. The old order was gone for ever. She turned round and looked at the beautiful Beechlands Mansion, that, like other big houses she had known, had probably, once, rung to the sound of parties and the rich cavorting about.

"No" she thought "things will never be the same again."

The following week Alice took Rosa on the train and bus. For her it was a big adventure and they took cakes and biscuits and some crayoning that Doris and Stanley had done. They found him in the garden with his leg propped up and with a couple of crutches. It was Rosa that spotted him. The bandage had been removed from his head but he had lost most of his thinning hair.

"There he is mother" she pointed "that's father." "I hope his head gets better soon" she whispered. "Oh what funny clothes they are all wearing."

He tried to get up, realised it was going to be more difficult than he thought and so sat down again.

"Hello Rosa dear!" he cried as she ran up to him. He put his arm around the child and felt better immediately. "I'll be home soon Kate" he said "just as soon as this ruddy leg is better and they decide that my brains are still all right." He felt his head and winced.

"I read in the newspaper that even the German Government are telling the Kaiser to bring the war to an end" said Alice, "and, and....." she laughed "they say the German Navy has gone on strike." There was laughter all around from those sitting in the late autumn sun.

"Now Rosa!" said Charles "I want you to tell me all about what you and your brother and sister have been doing." He sat and patiently listened to tales from school and about the flowers she had pressed and put in a book. Just the sound of her childish voice was like heaven compared with the whizz-bangs and carnage that he had witnessed. All he wanted to do now was forget it. All anybody in Beechlands wanted to do was to forget it.

"I remember the going and I remember the coming back" he said at a later time. "It's the bit in the middle that I would rather forget."

One of the nurses came and took Rosa for a game of catching the ball so that Alice and Charles had some time to themselves.

"You know one thing Kate" he whispered "the one thing I do want to do once all this is over. I want us to move nearer to London and make a fresh start. I want a fresh start in a small establishment where I can just do what I was always born to do – grow things."

"Well, we will see" replied Alice. It would be wonderful but all three children were at school and they had done enough moves. She wasn't going to argue with him just now though. Mrs. Browne-Douglas had been good to them, but things were changing and Charles was probably right. He usually was and, quite frankly, she would go anywhere he said right now.

"Hey look at this!" the cry came from one of the men sitting a few yards away with another group reading newspapers. All were in various stages of recovery and most had bandages about their person somewhere.

"It says here, "Confronted by the unstoppable strength of the Allies and faced with an outright Military defeat on the Western Front, General Ludendorff has suffered a nervous collapse at his headquarters and has lost all hope of victory...""

As one the men cheered and threw their caps in the air.

Rosa came running back to see what they were all so happy about.

"The nasty war will soon be over dear" said Alice and everything will be back to normal again."

Rosa wasn't quite sure what normal was any more.

Chapter Twelve Big Changes, 1918

The war officially ended at eleven o'clock on the 11th November just a few hours after the Armistice had been signed in a Railway Car at Compiegne in France. There were celebrations everywhere but these were muted by the slow and steady realisation of the numbers of dead and injured as the true cost of the war became evident. The figures in the papers varied but it was said that there had been seventeen million deaths and twenty million injured.

"I can't bring myself to celebrate" said Mrs. Browne-Douglas when Alice arrived at work. "Not with all these deaths. It makes you wonder whether things will ever be back to the way they were before 1914."

Alice could not help but agree. Things were not back to normal for her yet. The war may be over but Charles was not home and nor was he likely to be until he was fully recovered. One wondered too, whether the mind would ever recover from the sights it had seen.

She visited him as often as she could but, every time she went, there were still more wounded soldiers arriving and the nurses were kept busy around the clock.

It was the spring of 1919 when Charles finally arrived home and, ironically, it was Rosa who first saw him coming down the street. She was in her usual spot at the gate when she saw a figure in the uniform of a soldier. He limped a bit but he was a familiar figure. She did not know which way to run. Whether she should run towards him or run into the house to tell her mother. She had been fooled before. She had watched before and she had run towards somebody only to be mistaken. She ran into the house.

"Mother, mother, mother! Come and see. I think it is father coming down the road."

By the time Alice had dropped what she was doing and arrived at the gate, he was there and there was no doubt any more. She was followed by Stanley and, a less forthcoming, Doris. Alice and the two older children clung to him and he clutched them in his arms. Doris was not quite sure. She had been only three when he had left. She wasn't sure who this strange man was. She was six now.

He dropped his kit bag, stooped down and smiled and she gingerly came up to him. It would take time. It would take time for everyone. He looked around the little garden that came with the Tide Cottage.

"I can see I shall have to do some hedge trimming soon" he said "it grows so fast at this time of year."

Alice could not control the tears. "Come on" she said "the kettle is on the stove."

He picked up his bag. The one thing that came back with him that he did not lose was the photo that Alice had sent to him of her and the children in their best clothes. He took it out and popped it on the mantelpiece.

"You have grown since then" he said. "But now I don't need this photo because I can see you all."

◆ ◆ ◆

AT THE SAME TIME as Charles was arriving home at Redhill his friend Henry, who he had first worked with for the 'Red Earl Spencer' at Althorp House, and at Belton House, was arriving home in Manchester.

Henry's war had ended somewhat differently.

He had been a prisoner-of-war for four years and over most of that time, until the Germans took over control from the Turks, the men had been subjected to beatings, torture, hard labour and forced marches but in the autumn of 1918 things started to change. The Germans and the Turks were losing. Then one morning news arrived that all the Germans must depart from Turkey within twenty-four hours. The war was over but this news still had not reached Henry and his fellow prisoners-of-war. He continued to keep his diary and by now his exercise book was full of his memories.

"You never know" he said "one day, even if I am not around, somebody may find it."

He wrote:

"A hurried departure was witnessed. The Germans calling on fellows to volunteer to man the transport etc of which twenty men offered their services. A little while after I was informed by a Turkish officer that the war was over, the Turkish had surrendered and the Germans had made a hurried exit I could not understand at first or would not, because we had heard many times before that the war was over so of course I put no faith in it – yet on second thought I somewhat got guessing as the Germans had departed so suddenly. I resolved to take the news to our Captain Davis. When I asked him, he said "yes, there is something in the wind and I am doing my best to get to know what it is all about. However, leave it at that and whatever I hear, you all can rest assured old chap I will not delay a moment in telling you all I know."

I paid very little heed to the news, returned and continued on with my work. Two days later we were suddenly told to cease work and remain in our huts for further orders. One morning, as I sat wondering about this piece of news, – 'the war over – could it be possible?' a knock was heard on our hut door. I was greeted by the Commander's servant who told me the good news. I left him standing there and rushed out to inform Captain Davis of what I had heard.

"I will go over to the Commander my lad, and I hope and trust it is so."

THE 18TH NOVEMBER 1918

This day we were ordered to parade — every man to fall in by ten o'clock, at the German Mess Room (previously occupied by the Germans before their departure). "All present and correct Sir" said our Sergeant and our officers addressed us. This is something like the speech he gave.

"Now my lads I am in a fog — in the first place what beats me is the Germans going all of a hurry — second, you men suddenly called to leave work — thirdly, the rumours that are going about. I have interviewed the Commander and he has told me that all hostilities have ceased — an unconditional surrender of the Turkish Army. Also in a very short time I will be hearing definitely from the British Headquarters at Aleppo where our troops are at present — I am doing my best to get to know the news more surely and I will not rest until I can get the connections by wire or otherwise. I shall notify you of what news I get in the meantime. Go back men to your respective places. Keep a great heart — make whatever you wish of this good news but I wish to state avoid clashing with your enemies — keep your reputation as Britishers — be disciplined — be men — do not insult any Turkish Officer or man — be friends with each other and if, as I think is true, as true sportsmen never gloat over victory"

"Good old blighty, good old Captain" was the cry from the men.

That speech filled me with gladness — gladness that it had come at last after so long of waiting.

THE COLONEL'S ARRIVAL

Our captain had succeeded in getting to know the true facts of the previous day's rumours and a parade was ordered amid great cheers at three pm that day. Every one of us was eager to hear the news from our officer, a few words of which settled all, and which brought joy to boiling point. These were our officer's words,

"Men, I have succeeded in getting through to Aleppo and I am full" – with tears of joy in his eyes our Captain carried on under difficulties. He told us that our Commander-in-Chief was on his way to us at all speed of which he expected him this night so with expectations of a quick enquiry we awaited our Colonel's arrival.

Daisy, just picture the happiness surrounding our little camp after so many years of Hell. Think of it – we were alive and going home. Homeland, when I shall see you again – gladness – happiness – overwhelming joy. The coming night appeared like days to us but we patiently waited. We glanced eagerly towards the road, wondering and anxiously pining for the coming Officer in Command. Thus the longing – yes the longing – to be free. Yes, and the man that was coming here alone could prepare our liberty.

At last, could it be possible, yes the telephone told us that he had left the camp below. We strained our eyes for horses thinking he would come upon us in one mad gallop. Afterwards we were told to watch out for the powerful 'motor car' and we never took our eyes off the winding road he would travel to us.

The big lamp was giving a brilliant light. Everyone around seemed to be preparing as if for a great King. Every man on the verge of excitement could not keep still.

"Hang on, don't let it get you down," said a voice.

"Here he comes" was a wild cry.

Away, far away we could see the powerful lights of his motor car approaching I am sure he would hear our cheers — for every man poured forth his voice as he never did before. Slowly but surely that car crept towards us.

That big moving object was gradually creeping towards us as if new life. Then, as if the heavens above had opened, the big powerful car was upon us. We did not scatter — we hung on — we were eager to greet him and the armoured cars that accompanied him,

"Hurrah, hurrah, good old Colonel", the excitement was intense, Men hung on the foot boards as if mad — mad was not the word at this moment — it was gladness. They clung on to these cars as a drowning man would to a plank of wood — we gave them a grand reception.

Four armoured cars followed up in the rear. Men rushed to these crying "shake old sport - put it there — what's the news? — give us a blighty fag — a speech — silence — order." Could you obtain order from such heart torn men as us.

The sight of our Colonel and his men filled us with all the joy that there was in life, - yes, overwhelming gladness, but we wanted further news so listened anxiously to our Colonel who in settling down was given the opportunity of speech,

"Men of the British Regiments, I come with orders and to enquire as to the number of men that are here alive at present, Also for your speedy release and departure out of the hands of these people. I will do all in my power for a speedy removal of you as soon as I arrive back.

"Good old Colonel — three cheers! He's a jolly good fellow!" The cry from our men was heart rending — brave men wept tears of joy.

Soon, all over, we returned to our respective abodes amid encouraging remarks from our Turkish sentries who greeted us as we passed by. I may say that not one of us insulted or harmed any Turk whatever. We acted as true Britishers."

It was going to take a lot of time for the men, no matter where they had been at war, to get over the ordeal. For a few, for a very few, like Henry, the 'medicine' was to write it down, to get it down on paper and tell the story. For others, such as Charles, all he wanted to do was put it out of his mind. He said again...

"I remember the going Kate, and I remember the coming back, but it is the bit in the middle that I want to forget."

Alice fussed around him and gave him his favourite chair. All he wanted to do was sit and watch his children playing.

"This will do for me Kate," he said "this will do for me."

"Well, please God that the leaders of the world have learnt their lesson" said Alice, "and that there is never, ever, another war again.

◆ ◆ ◆

Although the war ended on the 11th November 1918 it was January 1919 before Henry finally arrived home. Charles had been home a few weeks when he received his friend's letter:

"When I got to Manchester I got the bus and was shocked that there were female conductors. It was early and on this misty morning, and after nearly five years I did not know where I lived. I enquired and was assisted to Earl Street. Entering this street I had speech with the 'knocker-up' man. No.4 was reached and his long pole began to play on the upstairs window, I urging him to do so, pressing a shilling in his hand saying "Go on – knock until she comes down." Then I heard Daisy's voice.

"All right, all right, what ails you – have you gone mad?" she cried.

"It's me!" I answered when she opened the door.

"Good God Henry – is it you?"

"Yes dear, it is me."

On hearing my words, her feet lingered a little and then she fainted in front of me. I assisted her as best I could and with my kisses on her dear face I waited for her to revive.

Thank God, we are all back safe with our families and to do our gardening again. I'll tell you one thing Charles my friend. I will not be volunteering for more adventures.

Regards, Henry."

Charles finished reading. "Five years!" he said. "Five years he has been away! Three was bad enough. No wonder poor Daisy fainted. He carefully folded the letter up and put it behind the clock.

"That just about sums it up Charles" said Alice. "Poor Henry is nearly forty isn't he."

"Well, he wasn't when he went. All he wanted to do was have some adventures and send money back for Daisy and the children. I said he was mad at the time."

"Let's hope that nobody ever has to do it again," said Alice. "The Crimean, The Boer War, and now this. All those lives ruined. Surely, surely it couldn't happen again. Could it?"

The sound of the children's voices came from the bedroom as Stanley and Doris argued with each other while Rosa tried to settle them down.

"Come on, be quiet and let daddy get some peace" she said "and if you are good I will read you a story."

Slowly, very, very slowly, things were beginning to get back to normal.

CHAPTER XIII

Coxhill Manor, Chobham 1920

Alice looked on as her three children ran up the path and round the back of the Gardener's Cottage at Coxhill, Chobham in Surrey. She had been sorry to leave Redhill because Jessie Brown-Douglas had been very kind to her but things were changing rapidly. The large estate had been sold to the Government and was still being used for the wounded from the War.

"These large houses are becoming more and more expensive to keep Alice" Jessie had said when they last met. "People are selling up and getting smaller places or else investing in industry. It's all change everywhere since the war ended."

Mr. Browne-Douglas and Charles had scoured the newspapers together and, eventually found Coxhill Manor which was owned by Mr. Christopher Gabriel, a Timber Merchant of some repute in the City of London.

"I know him well" said Charles's employer "I will put a word in for you and I will give you a good reference." "Besides..." he went on "nobody is going to turn down one of our War Heroes."

"Huh, I don't know that I am any war hero" said Charles "all I did was the job I was called up for Sir – no bloody choice."

The idea of going up to Chobham appealed to him though. He needed a new start. He would never, ever forget the carnage of The Somme, although he tried hard enough, any more than Henry would forget the Dardanelles and being a prisoner-of-war, but a new start in a smaller establishment might help. It had been six months since he had got back from Chailey Green and now he felt able to take control again and sort out the future for his family, and maybe, just maybe, live happily ever after, like it says in the children's books. Besides, Alice had given him some news. It was news that meant they would need a bigger bungalow. They were expecting their fourth child in the spring.

Mr. Browne-Douglas had arranged for a motor van to take their luggage, and the family took the train to Woking and then bus to Chobham. It had been exciting for the children but Alice was exhausted and starting to feel the presence of the new baby in her womb. She just felt very glad when the bus arrived outside the little bungalow in the tree lined street. Charles had still not fully recovered. He was slowly improving but the war had changed him. Gone was the happy smiling lad that she had met at the Christmas party at Easthampstead Park who loved to play the accordion. She knew the 'old' Charles was inside him somewhere, and he still had the twinkle in his eyes, but it would be some considerable time, if ever, before it would re-appear.

"Thank you very much" she said to the bus conductor when the vehicle stopped right outside the door.

"We are going to live here" piped up Doris. "In that house there."

"Well I hope you will be very happy." They all watched as the bus trundled on its way into the village of Chobham.

"They have come a long way since the horse drawn ones" said Alice as it disappeared out of sight.

"Not so good for the roses though" said Charles "it was always good to have the manure for the roses."

"Mr. and Mrs. Ratcliff?" Their conversation was disturbed by the arrival of a tall dark haired man who had just crossed the road from the bungalow opposite.

Coxhill Manor.

"Hello! I am William Mumford, the Butler for Mr. and Mrs. Gabriel," he said. "I just saw you arrive. The old man has given me the key to the house to pass on to you. I live just across the road there. If there is anything I can do for you, anything at all, please come over."

"Thank you" said Alice as Charles took the key."

"The wife would have popped over" William Mumford went on, "but she is feeding our new baby – she is our only one. We have called her Edna."

"How lovely!" replied Alice.

"Anyway, I will leave you in peace" he said "but I have put a few things in the larder for you such as bread and cheese as well as a few bits and pieces from the village shop.

"Oh how kind of you Mr. Mumford. Thank you. How much do we owe you?"

"Nothing," he replied. "Mrs. Gabriel has paid for it and you are welcome". He doffed his hat and walked back over the road.

"Oh, isn't that nice of him Charles?" she cried.

They were suddenly disturbed by seven year old Doris.

"Mummy, mummy," she squealed as she came running round the corner from the back of the house. "There is a real toilet, a real one with a chain!" Then she stopped. "Only I can't reach it."

Alice laughed. "Don't worry. We will put a string on it for you."

They went into the house. The next day Charles would be reporting for duty at Coxhill Manor and he hoped that it would be for ever.

The children ran around the bungalow exploring while Alice and Charles unpacked. It was one of two cottages that were situated on the same side of the road, about fifty yards from each other and separated by gardens, both owned by the Gabriel estate in addition to the one opposite and used by the Butler. There was a large kitchen with a big wooden table in the middle and big chairs either side of the kitchen range. It was also a living area because that was where the warmth was in the house. There was also a small parlour plus two big bedrooms. Alice had already decided that the parlour would have to be a bedroom. However, she had fallen in love with the place. She stood at the kitchen sink and looked across the field at the back of the house. It was a field that was the short cut to the back of Coxhill Manor. "It's beautiful!" she said simply.

Doris had been right. There was a flush toilet and it was only a few yards across from the house. Not right down the bottom of the garden as she had been used to. True, most of the houses where she had worked had proper plumbing but the Tide Cottages didn't. They usually had 'thunder buckets' as Charles insisted on calling them, Tin buckets that were emptied once a week. This was sheer luxury.

Charles had already found his way to a big armchair situated by the kitchen range.

"This will do for me" he grunted as he got up again. "I can't sit here yet though. I shall go and find out if there is any coal in the coal hole and then get the fire lit. Then we can put the kettle on."

Alice laughed. "Look" she chuckled "we have got a proper oven now. We can put the kettle on that."

"Hmm" Charles grunted, "I am not so sure about that. How do we know it works?"

"Well I am just about to find out." She spotted a jar full of spills and some matches and proceeded to light the stove.

"Dangerous things if you ask me" said Charles "I prefer the good old kitchen range like this."

He stalked off out into the garden. He still had a bit of a limp. The children were already exploring the bedrooms.

Alice laughed and let him go. She wasn't going to argue. He had a point though. The children had never been in a house with a modern oven before. They had always had a kitchen range. She would have to keep an eye on them until they got used to the idea.

The Mumfords had indeed stocked the larder and there was everything there that she needed to feed her family on this first day in their new home.

The following day Alice watched Charles cross the field and go through the gate at the top. He was on his way to meet his new employers, Mr. and Mrs. Gabriel.

◆ ◆ ◆

CHARLES CROSSED THE TOP of the drive that lead to the back gardens of Coxhill Manor. Times were changing but not that much. It wasn't the right thing for servants to go to the front door. He crossed the carefully manicured vegetable patches and walked up to the back door. He had put on his gardening boots and was carrying his big black apron with the large pocket which he had worn for his work all his life. He passed a couple of young lads who were busy chopping back a hedge. They reminded him of himself fifteen or more years ago.

An older man was clipping away at the ivy covering one of the walls of the house.

"Hello old chap, you must be Ratcliff" he said. He put his clippers into the pocket of his apron and came and shook Charles's hand.

"I'm Alfred" he went on. "Mr. Gabriel told me you were coming. I hear you were in the war old chap?"

"I'd rather forget all about it" said Charles.

"Thank God it's over!" exclaimed Alfred ignoring the request. "Such carnage, such carnage!"

So this was the fellow he would be working with. He was a little chap, probably in his early fifties.

"I'd rather forget it" Charles persevered "except on Remembrance Day of course."

"Yes, that was a good idea to have a Remembrance Day" chattered Alfred "The King is going to unveil this new Cenotaph thing in Whitehall in November you know."

"I know" said Charles patiently. "I had better go and meet my new employers now or I shall get the sack before I start."

"I live in the other Tide Cottage, it's called The Lodge. Sorry, I beat you to it, it is the larger of the two cottages and we have been here a few years now. Strictly speaking it should be yours, because you will be the Head Gardener one day." He paused for a minute as if thinking. "That is if you stop here of course. It may seem quiet after being in the Army."

Charles was beginning to wonder if he was ever going to shut him up.

"I am happy with quiet" smiled Charles cynically. Even now, people did not really know what went on in the Great War. *"He really hasn't a clue"* he thought.

He was quite happy with The Gardener's Cottage, besides 'age has its privileges' and Alfred was clearly a good ten years older than him. Of course this place was nothing like the size of anything that he and Alice had been used to but it was big enough and it would do for him. He loved the idea of being Head Gardener but there was plenty of time. Despite everything that had happened to him he was not yet forty. Alfred read his thoughts.

"You are but a youngster yet" he said "plenty of time for you."

"I really must go" insisted Charles.

"Yes, and I must get on with sorting out this Ivy. Looks like Cook is waiting for you anyway."

He looked along to the back door to see a very large lady waiting for him with arms folded across her ample chest.

"What is it about cooks" thought Charles "that they always have ample chests?"

"Good morning Mr. Ratcliff" she smiled. "Come into the kitchen and I shall send Sally to let Madam know you are here." She was disturbed by two small boys who came running downstairs and started to have a look on the kitchen table.

"Have you got any biscuits Cook?" said one little fair haired chap that looked about the same age as Stanley.

"You shoo off Master John and Master Ralph." She pretended to chase them with her rolling pin. "Off you go and leave my kitchen alone. Aren't you supposed to be at school?"

She was aided in her quest to get rid of them by the arrival of the lady of the house. She was a tall, very imposing looking woman with steely grey hair. Charles judged her to be in her forties. She was wearing a long navy blue day dress with a lacy collar. *"I wonder if my mother made that lace"* he thought to himself.

"Go on, take heed of Cook, off to school with you." The children ran off and she shook hands with Charles.

"Welcome to Coxhill Manor" she smiled "I am so sorry that my husband is not here. He is up in London today." Then she lowered her voice. "I do hope you have recovered completely from the war. Such a dreadful, awful thing. All those lives lost and all those people injured."

He really did not want a repeat of the conversation he had just had with Alfred.

"Thank you Madam" he replied. "I shall look forward to doing the best I can for you.

A couple of young girls appeared, who were clearly Parlour Maids, and the Cook started cutting up some meat for dinner. The kitchen, though smaller, was much the same as every other kitchen of every big estate that he had worked at, and he had worked at quite a few by now.

"Alfred Baker is our Head Gardener and lives in The Lodge, but.." and she lowered her voice again. "He can talk for England!"

"I noticed Madam" smiled Charles. He felt a twinge in his leg where his wound had been. It had been eighteen months now and still it hurt if he stood in a certain way. As to the shrapnel in his head, well the dent was still there, but he was going bald now and he would just plonk his trilby hat on that would be that.

"Anyway, Alfred will look after you," She lowered her voice again "though I don't think there will be much he can tell you, not looking at *your* credentials. I see you have worked at Althorp House up in Northampton and at Aldermaston. They are both very prestigious establishments Charles."

He nodded politely and then took his leave of Mrs. Gabriel and went out to find Alfred. She hurried off to find Ralph and John. The chauffeur had turned up at the front of the house to take them to school.

He could see that the gardens were quite large. Of course, nowhere near on the scale of Belton or Aldermaston, but plentiful enough and he could imagine that there would be plenty to keep the staff of two senior gardeners and six lads busy. As he came out of the back door there was a large pond full of goldfish and an area given over to roses. Then to his left the kitchen garden seemed full of vegetables. The family certainly didn't mean to go short and there would be plenty left over which could end up in the village shops.

Alfred had now walked round to the side of the house and was in the herb garden.

"I love it here" said Alfred as Charles approached "when this lavender is in flower it bowls you over."

Despite Charles's efforts to shut it out of his mind he couldn't help but think of the awful acres of mud, bomb craters and blackened trees that he had experienced such a short time ago. The comparison to this beautiful garden was stark.

"Oh why to they do it?" he said to himself for the millionth time since 1915.

"It looks like it is very well kept" he said, looking around while Alfred was talking to him.

"Yes, Mr. Gabriel owns it all, and," he gestured across to somewhere in the distance "he also owns the farm over there at Deep Pool. I expect that will be Master Ralph's one day".

"Oh I think I saw Master Ralph and Master John just now" replied Charles.

"Yes, young mischief makers, the pair of them. He has two older children as well. There is Master Chris who will probably take over his Timber business one day. I think he is about eighteen, and then there is Miss Enid, the daughter."

By the time Alfred had finished Charles thought he knew all there was to know about the Gabriel family. He unrolled his black apron and tied the tapes round his waist to secure it. He was bigger and thicker set now and it didn't wrap around him twice as it had done when he was a teenager.

"Well, I had better start as I mean to go on" he said "I'll go and check out the greenhouses."

It was, he hoped, the start of the rest of his life. Moreover, there was a new little baby on the way. Life was starting to get sweeter again.

◆ ◆ ◆

THE LEAVES ON THE trees around Coxhill were starting to turn golden brown and the lavender was in full bloom when, in September, little Edith Joan Ratcliff was born. As far as the children were concerned she, sort of, 'appeared'. Even Rosa at eleven was still not really aware of her mother's ever expanding stomach. Then they came home from school to find the doctor and the midwife at the house and their mother in bed with the bedroom door tight shut. Charles shooed them off out to play while he waited for the new arrival.

"Go on, off with you. You stay out of the way for the time being. Your Mother is in good hands."

"What on earth is going on?" said Stanley as the children ran out into the field.

"I think Mother is having a baby" said Rosa. "She had a baby inside her tummy and now they are getting it out."

Stanley and Doris thought their sister was just making up stories and they ran off to climb the big tree in the centre of the field whilst Rosa walked back to the house. She was just in time to hear her mother give a scream and then there was much rushing around.

Suddenly the door opened and it was Charles beaming all over his face.

"You have a new little sister Rosa" he said "you can go and tell the others now."

The children had not been home from school for long but in actual fact the labour had lasted most of the day.

"Stanley, Doris!" shouted Rosa, "we have a new little sister." The children scrambled down from the tree and rushed into the house.

"Wash your hands first" said the midwife "go on now, all of you, wash your hands. You too Mr. Ratcliff!"

Charles meekly did as he was told and then the family gathered round to see the new little baby lying in an exhausted Alice's arms.

"Where has she come from?" said Doris.

"I don't know" said Stanley, "she wasn't here this morning."

Nobody attempted to answer their questions and soon they gave up and went off to play. Everyone was overjoyed and letters went off to Alice's sisters and her father Joshua and also to Elizabeth and John Ratcliff in Pitsford to tell them they had another little granddaughter.

"We shall call her Edith Joan" said Alice, "Edith after my sister Edie and Joan after my niece."

Charles didn't mind what she was called. Doris Emily and Rosa were already called after his sisters and Stanley after a street! It was time that Alice had another choice.

"We will be able to have her christened at St. Lawrence Church in Chobham," said Charles.

They had already started to attend the Church and the children were in the Sunday School.

Alice looked closely into the new baby's face. Who did she look like? She didn't look like any of the other children. She looked different somehow. She began to start to feel a little uncomfortable, but she kept her thoughts to herself. Everyone was so excited and happy and already the little girls were fighting over who was going to look after her.

At first all seemed fine. She seemed healthy enough but Alice was still not sure. She didn't look right somehow. Maybe it was a Mother's intuition – call it what you will, but her fears were confirmed on her first visit to the Children's Clinic in the village.

"I am afraid your baby has Downs Syndrome Mrs. Ratcliff."

"Downs Syndrome?" Alice had never heard the expression before.

"It is what we used to call mongolism" the Doctor went on, "we don't use that phrase now though. The correct phrase is Downs Syndrome."

Alice knew straight away what mongolism was and that was the suspicion that she had tried to ignore. She remembered when she was a child that a neighbour's baby was like it and they couldn't send her to school. She didn't care about the name, not just then. Everybody called it mongolism.

"I am sure she will be all right" said the doctor kindly as Alice sat down in the nearest chair in shock. "She will have more difficulty learning and could have some difficulties as she gets older, but she is quite healthy at the moment."

"Huh, well that is reassuring" thought Alice cynically.

"Also, she may be more subject to picking up illnesses" he said.

Alice thought she was in the middle of a nightmare and it was with a heavy heart that she put little Edie in the pram and walked down the road back towards the little bungalow at Coxhill. She was thinking how she was going to tell Charles and the children.

She let herself into the house and put the baby in her cot. Her peace did not last for long. Rosa came flying in, only to get changed out of her school clothes and rush out again. She didn't notice the redness around her mother's eyes.

"I am going to join the Girl Guides" she said excitedly "I am meeting my friend Mavis in the village and we are going to the Church Hall together."

"Well stop and have a sandwich first Rosa" said Alice, hastily brushing away a stray tear.

Rosa ate a sandwich and got ready at the same time.

"Careful you will get indigestion."

Then the peace was totally shattered by the arrival of Stanley and Doris together. Alice decided that the nine year old and seven year old did not really need to know about Edie's condition just yet and Rosa was already out of the door in her quest to join the Girl Guides.

It didn't alter the fact though that she still had to tell Charles and she made up her mind to wait until the children were in bed.

Once they had their cocoa and Rosa had excitedly told everyone about her first visit to the Girl Guides, Alice settled her and Stanley down to read their books for a while and then she read a story to Doris. As she tucked them in, and they said their prayers, she gave thanks that she had been blessed with such lovely healthy children.

When the children were in bed she could contain her tears no longer and had to tell Charles the bad news about his baby daughter.

"Downs Syndrome!" roared Charles when she told him. He thumped his fist down on the table and the cutlery rattled in the drawer. "That's mongolism isn't it?"

"They don't call it that any more Charles" said Alice, they call it Downs Syndrome!"

"Huh!" mumbled Charles. "Just because it has got a new fangled name it doesn't alter anything."

Then he put his arms around her and let her cry into his shoulder.

"Don't worry Kate my love" he said "we will look after her no matter what she has. She is still our little daughter."

He went and picked the baby up. She was such a dear little thing. His face softened and the initial shock subsided.

"Well Kate, poor little Edie, we will look after her and we will love her just the same as the others. It's not her fault, It's not anybody's fault." He looked down at her face. "Don't you worry little one."

"The doctor said that she would be more susceptible to diseases" Alice told him, "so we will have to be especially careful with her."

"We will make sure she doesn't get any diseases" grunted Charles.

Little Edie.

He put her back down in her cot and she slept peacefully. He did wonder though, just how many more things were going to happen before his family could live happily ever after.

"There is no need to tell the children yet," said Alice as she made his cup of cocoa. "There is plenty of time for that."

She had hoped that she might do a few Parlour Maid duties for Mr. and Mrs. Gabriel once the children were bigger, but suddenly she realised that, from now on, her days of working for the gentry were over.

CHAPTER XIV

The End of an Era, 1929

As Alice busied herself getting the tea ready she reflected upon the past nine years. All in all it had been a good nine years and Edie's Down's syndrome condition had not spoilt it.

There had been many developments since they set up home in the little cottage on the edge of the Coxhill Estate. Not least of these had been the wireless. Charles had always wanted one, but, for a long time it was just something that the gentry had and it also cost money. Eventually though he had 'splashed out', as Alice put it, and he had invested in a nice shiny brown wooden cased wireless in time for the Christmas of 1928. She smiled to herself. He was so thrilled with it, but she wasn't going to touch the thing. No fear! She couldn't get used to the idea of somebody speaking out of a box in your own home. Besides, whenever she did try to turn the knobs the darn thing spluttered at her. No, she would leave it to the men.

There had been one bit of sadness in the past year though, when news that her brother-in-law, Laney's husband died.

"Oh poor Laney" cried Alice when she got the news. "She had only been married ten years!"

Now with Joshua also on his own, he and his daughter moved in together to a house at Mitcham which wasn't too far away and comparatively easy for the family to visit on the train.

Stanley was thrilled that his father had finally got a wireless. He had grown into a strapping, good looking lad of seventeen with the black wavy hair favoured by his mother. He had been working as an errand boy since leaving school and also learning to drive and be a mechanic. His one ambition though was to join the new and exciting RAF that had so recently been formed from the Royal Flying Corps and the Royal Naval Air Service. With the memories of the Great War still fresh in his mind Charles had misgivings but his son had been mad on aeroplanes ever since he was little and he first saw one flying overhead at Redhill.

"Darn things!" exclaimed Charles when one had spluttered overhead and Stanley rushed out to see it. "If the good Lord had meant us to fly he would have given us wings."

Now Christmas had passed and it was the year 1929. Alice stood at the back window and watched Charles and Rosa walking through the snow towards the house. Rosa was nearly twenty years old now and a good looking slim girl, full of life. She helped up at the Manor these days, alternating between working in the gardens with Charles in the summer, or, during the winter waiting on Mr. and Mrs. Gabriel. She had a few boys in the village who took an interest in her but didn't seem anxious to walk out with anyone.

Alice put the kettle on the stove ready to give them a warm drink when they got in. Little Edie played happily on the floor with her dollies. She had all sorts of learning difficulties but she was dearly loved and, at nine, had turned into a lovely affectionate little girl.

Only Doris was away from home in this first month of 1929. She had a job training to be a Cook at a mansion in nearby Woking and just came home at weekends.

It had been a blissful nine years since they arrived. Other than the initial sadness at Edie's condition, there had been nothing to mar anything about the little paradise they had moved to. Charles had met Mr. Christopher Gabriel soon after arriving and professed him to be a 'decent chap'. He loved his work and he was given free rein of all the gardens and greenhouses.

Alice watched as Rosa and Charles stopped and he crossed over the field to check his bees while she waited for him. It hadn't been long, after they came here to Coxhill, that he took up keeping bees, the hobby that, so long ago, had been started when he had been with Bill at Aldermaston. He bought two beehives and initially put them among the bushes in the garden.

"Oh no, you can't have them there Charles" objected Alice. "It's much too near to where Edie might be playing." She was right of course. Alice was always right. In the end Charles got permission to put them along the side of Mr. Gabriel's field.

"Just so long as I get some of the honey Ratcliff" Mr. Gabriel laughed.

Now Charles had nine beehives. He had bought one a year.

At the same time Alice, along with Mrs. Gabriel joined the Women's Institute which was just starting up in Chobham. It became an outlet for all the honey that Charles and his bees were able to produce and, of course, increased their income.

He was never still for long, up at the crow of the cockerel and working in the gardens all day. Then, with every other spare minute he had he worked on his own large garden that was attached to the bungalow. Alice never wanted for fruit and vegetables and her grocery list when she went to the village was really quite small. They certainly lived up to the motto of Charles's mother, "if you can't make it or grow it then it is not worth having."

She watched as he rejoined Rosa and they crossed the field and came through the gate into the back yard. Soon they were indoors and kicked their boots off.

"They had quite a house full today" Rosa said. "Master Ralph was there and Miss Enid and Master Kit." Kit was the nickname for Christopher Gabriel's oldest son, who was also called Christopher. "Master John was there as well. There is talk of him going into the Army."

"Huh! Well lord help him then" grunted Charles as he sat down in his chair and cuddled Edie. "At least Stanley is talking about doing something that is relatively safe as long as he doesn't decide to be a pilot or something daft like that."

"I don't know about that" said Alice "if there were a war he wouldn't be safe."

"There won't be any war. It is certainly a good way of learning a trade anyway, especially in Peacetime."

Talk of the Army caused him to think about his old friend Henry. They had kept in touch but as time had gone on it wasn't very often. He never really got over his time as a Prisoner-of-War at the hands of the Turks and had difficulty in settling down to any job. The last Charles heard he was working on a farm. Even now, eleven years on, the dead were still being brought back and nobody ever would know the real cost. Not just the cost in lives and the wounded, but those with mental scars and shell shock that would last for ever. It would be generations before people would ever have any idea of what they all went through.

Alice couldn't help wondering what the next few years would bring now that the children were all grown up. Coxhill was a far cry from the sumptuous Easthampstead Park or Hillsborough Castle, but she wouldn't have it any different. Then there had been the nightmare of the Great War, but Charles had settled down now. He would never fully recover and she noticed the differences in his demeanour. The laughing and happy young man that played the accordion at the staff party had gone, but deep down the softness was still there and that came out when he cuddled Edie. They still had the accordion, tucked away somewhere but that's where it stayed, 'out of sight and out of mind'.

The sound of the gate clanging and a cheery whistle was an indication that Stanley was also home from work. He was always guaranteed to liven anywhere up and he put Alice so much in mind of the seventeen year old that she met all those years ago. The room seemed to light up at his presence as he took off his scarf and gloves and slumped down near the fire.

"Brrr, it's cold out there tonight" he laughed "I've done nothing else but dodge people throwing snowballs today." He looked down at Edie. "Hello Edie my love, come and give your big brother a cuddle. I need a nice warm." Edie ran over to him and put her arms round him and gave him a big hug.

◆ ◆ ◆

THE FIRST EXCITEMENT OF the year came with a sighting of the R101 just before Easter. All the primroses were out, and the buttercups and daisies in the field, which were so ideal for the bees, seemed to be more plentiful than ever. Charles and Rosa spent the day, along with Alfred and the rest of the gardening staff, pricking out stuff from the greenhouse and planting out. It had been a busy day but a happy one and the pair of them had a spring in their step as they walked down the back drive on their way home for tea. It was Charles's intention to cut across the field and check the beehives on the way as usual. Suddenly there was a deep whirring sound which seemed to come from right above them.

"What the devil!" gasped Charles. They both looked up to see the R101 airship steadily gliding overhead. It wasn't the first time he had seen one. They had been used during the war to drop bombs and also to carry capsules underneath from which a soldier could fire guns at the enemy. What he did not expect to see was one flying over the drive at Coxhill even though he had heard on the News that they were being tested for passenger use from RAF Cardington. Not that there were any passengers on this one because it did not have the capsule or gondolier, as they called it, underneath. It was a rare sight.

"Good lord alive, I never thought I would ever see one of those things again?" he cried. He thought quickly though.

"Rosa, Rosa, quick run into the house and get the camera," He commanded. "You can run faster than me." Twenty years ago he would have run her off her feet but not any more.

Rosa was standing transfixed but dashed off and came running back before the airship could disappear out of sight, and this time with Alice and Edie close behind her.

"Now there is a sight you do not see often!" remarked Charles as he took his picture. He just managed to take it before it disappeared over the trees and slowly made its way in an easterly direction.

Suddenly Stanley appeared, rushing down the drive on his bike. He leapt off and threw it against the grass verge.

"Did you see the airship? Did you see it?"

"That's what the Germans were using to drop bombs on us all," said Charles. "It's nice to see one without someone throwing things from it."

" I want to join the RAF when I am old enough" Stan said for the umpteenth time.

Charles knew that he would be old enough this year. Alice wasn't very happy but it did seem inevitable.

"Well I should not like to think of you going in one of those things" she said.

"No mother" he laughed "I would go in as a driver. I don't think they would let me loose with one of those."

The RAF had gone from strength to strength since the war and it was every boys dream, including their son's, to be in this new and up and coming branch of His Majesty's services.

R101 test flight over Coxhill.

Little did anyone know, as they all went into the house, and Charles switched his precious wireless on for the News, that in little over a year Stanley would be among the guard of honour bringing back the dead when the very airship, that they had just photographed, crashed, killing everyone on board.

◆ ◆ ◆

A FEW DAYS LATER they received news that would upset everybody. Alice's beloved father, Joshua Kirck, had passed away. It came in the form of a telegram from Laney. The funeral took place at Barnes, in the very church where he had been a Lay Reader until his move to live with his daughters at Mitcham, and he was buried in the cemetery there. The whole family went on the train for the occasion.

"Oh, it is the end of an era Laney" said Alice, when they all went back to the house afterwards. "Now we are the older generation. It doesn't seem possible."

They were joined by Edith and her husband Wilfred. They had come all the way from the Channel Islands where they had settled since their marriage.

"Such a blow" said Edith "he was a good age though. Seventy-eight."

"Yes, poor old father" replied Laney "he never really got over the death of mother and young Charlie you know."

"Oh well, life goes on" said Edith, "and life is so much better now with all the modern things we have. It only seems like five minutes ago that we had horses all over the place on the streets of London."

"I don't know which is worse" laughed Alice "the smell of the manure or the smell of the fumes from the motor cars."

"You should be where we are in the Channel Islands" said Edith, "right on the sea front."

"That would be good for Rosa" said Alice "it might cure that cough she always seems to have these days."

Edith nodded towards where the younger members of the family were all gathered together with their cousins. "What of Rosa and Doris? What are they up to these days?"

"Doris is training to be a Cook" said Alice, "but to be honest Edith, I don't know what to do about Rosa. I'd like to get her into a big estate like I was, but they are all disappearing now. People can't maintain them any more and they are sold off to the Government."

"How would she like to come and live in Jersey with Wilfred and I" said Edith suddenly. "You know we run the tea rooms there. We could do with a waitress to help us, and we have our daughter Joan who would be some company for her."

Alice was quite taken aback. It was a good opportunity.

"What's all this?" They were interrupted by Charles. "What are you ladies cooking up."

She told him what Edith had just suggested.

"Hmm" he mused "well, that would be up to her Kate. I suppose it's all right as long as Edie looks after her."

"Of course my sister would look after her" said Alice. She got up from her seat and went and called Rosa away from the group. The whoop of joy said it all.

"Jersey! Everybody, I am going to live in Jersey with Aunt Edie' "

As Rosa went running off and Charles went to join the men, Edith turned to Alice with a smile. "Don't you get fed up with him calling you Kate?"

"No I am used to it now Edie', laughed Alice "a rose by any other name....."

What was a very sad occasion ended with a few smiles among the tears.

Of course, there were arrangements to be made, packing to do and Mr. and Mrs. Gabriel to be told, but within a few weeks, Wilfred and Edie came and paid another visit to see Laney and then called on Alice and Charles.

An excited Rosa packed her bags and hugged everybody.

"I will write as soon as I get there" she said.

Doris arrived on her bicycle so that she could see her sister off and Stan carried Rosa's suitcase for her and passed it to Wilfred to load onto the bus.

"Well, I expect the next one will be Stanley" said Charles as he put his arm around Alice's shoulders and they walked down the path after seeing them off. Stanley and Doris had already taken Little Edie indoors.

There was time for a short chat but soon Doris was making ready to leave.

"I have to go now, otherwise I will have Cook giving me the sack" she said and she ran and collected her bike from where she had left it by the wall. She gave each of her family a quick kiss and was off down the road, racing to get back before some dark clouds overhead decided to drop their load.

"It doesn't seem like five minutes ago since it was us leaving our homes does it Charles?" said Alice.

"Well, we were younger than them!" he replied "so we have done well really."

They walked into the house and Charles caught sight of his face in the reflection in the window. He thought of what Alice had just said about it not seeming like five minutes ago.

"Oh yes it does" he laughed "look at that grey hair."

A couple of weeks later Rosa sent them a photograph of the little café that Wilfred had taken.

It was just six days after his eighteenth birthday on 29th October that Stanley joined the RAF. However, first of all there had to be a family visit to Elizabeth and John Ratcliff in Northampton. Both were getting old now but Elizabeth still continued with her Lace Making.

"It's so much easier now I have the electric light" she said when Alice remarked about the fineness of her work, "Though I still prefer to work out at the front in the daylight if I can."

They had recently moved to a larger house. It was not very far away but it was more up to date and had the electric light and running water.

"Oh I don't know where I am these days Alice, what with all this modern stuff. I'm not complaining though" she laughed. "I even have a dust collector now."

"I know" replied Alice. "It is certainly easier than a dustpan and brush and all that bending about."

Elizabeth gazed at her grandchildren.

"Goodness me, you are all so big and grown up now."

Very soon the house filled up with Charles's brothers John and Joseph and their wives as well as Mabel with her new husband, Henry Hollowell.

"This is a real gathering of the clan" said John. "I think we shall have to charge our glasses and have a toast to us all and to young Stanley here." He bustled round filling the glasses with home made wine. "To everyone and especially to Stanley. Stay safe and good luck my boy."

"Nothing's changed" grinned Charles to himself "that's my parents – if you can't make it or grow it, then it's not worth having including the wine!" Little did he realise it but he was already just the same!

The men went off into a little huddle of their own whilst the ladies put the tea on the table.

"I suppose this is my brother Joseph's bread" said Mabel. "I've always liked his bread."

"Yes, they do well at that Bakers" said Elizabeth. "Joe is in charge of the shop now, he has done very well."

"Well I hope young Stan will do well in the RAF" said Emmie, "he is such a nice lad."

"Well, just so long as there are no more wars. That's the main thing." said Alice.

"Oh, I know dear." Emmie's face fell. "Poor Charles certainly went through it in the last lot didn't he. We were so lucky that John and Joe were too old to go but we lost cousins and no family was untouched." She leaned over to Alice and whispered "does he ever talk much about it?"

"No" replied Alice "never. He says he can remember the going and he can remember the coming back but it's the bit in the middle that he wants to forget."

In the next room John was pouring out another glass of wine for the men while the younger ones went off out into the garden.

"It's this chap Hitler that I am not happy about" he said quietly "I've been reading all about it and that Stock Market crash in the United States affected Germany badly. That upstart is playing on it."

"I don't understand" said Joseph.

"Well it seems that the Americans have called in all their foreign loans and it has crippled Germany. It's caused a lot of anger among this up and coming Nazi Party and Hitler is stirring them up."

"I agree" said Charles "I don't like it when the Germans get stirred up and, by all accounts that Nazi Party are a load of hooligans."

The younger members of the family left the older ones to their discussions and went out into the garden in the sunshine with little Edie as the centre of attention. Everybody wanted a cuddle from Edie and everybody got one.

"Pity Rosa is not here said Barry who was Joseph's son but I bet it is fun in the Channel Islands. I'd like to go there one day."

"Oh, I expect she is dancing the night away!" laughed Stan.

"Well good luck to you anyway Stanley" said his cousin Violet. "I think you are very brave."

"There is nothing brave about it" he replied as he cuddled Edie "the worst part will be missing home, but I am going to be a driver, not a pilot."

The discussion was brought to a swift conclusion by Elizabeth calling them for tea.

"Come on everyone, tea time! Jelly and cake!" They didn't need telling twice.

CHAPTER XV

Dark Days, 1929

I t was with a heavy heart that Alice stood outside the little Tide Cottage and watched Stanley go off on the bus to report for his recruit training at RAF Uxbridge. It was, however, a heavy heart mixed with pride. All the family were there to see him off. Rosa was home on a visit and she stood outside the cottage at the side of Doris and with her arm around Edie and waved. Charles helped him on with his case and then went back to join the little group. For Rosa, she couldn't help but remember back to when she had waved goodbye to her father and then returned each day to the same spot expecting to see him return. Now she knew better. He would return in the fullness of time. After all, there were no wars to stop him.

As for Alice, she felt exactly as her mother-in-law must have felt when her seventeen year old boy went off to Lincoln. It was the end of a chapter, or another chapter beginning.

For Rosa it has been an exciting time.

"Oh it's been so exciting" she said as soon as they were settled after seeing Stanley off. "The ferry from Portsmouth all the way to Jersey was wonderful and it is such a beautiful Island. The tea rooms are overlooking the beach and aeroplanes come down and land there right in front of the café. They carry as many as six passengers at any one time."

Alice went out to the well in the garden, where she kept her butter and milk in the summer, to bring some in for tea. The well wasn't used for water any more but it was very useful to put cold stuff in the bucket and lower it down to keep cool. Of course, with Little Edie in mind, Charles had made a lid as a cover so that nobody could fall in. It had a hole in the middle for the rope to go through and made in two halves so that it could open up. Alice opened it and fetched up what she needed for tea and then carefully lowered the bucket and replaced the lid. All the time she was thinking of Stanley. She was pleased for him but it was a very unstable world these days.

"Oh don't be so stupid Alice" she said to herself. "Pull yourself together woman."

She went back indoors where Rosa was still chatting excitedly about her stay at the 'Bon Viveur' with Wilfred and Edie' and cousin Joan.

By the end of the year Stan had finished his Recruit training and was posted to Cardington in Bedfordshire. When he came home in his uniform for the first time Alice was struck at the likeness between him and her young brother Charlie who had been killed so tragically on The Somme and her heart skipped a beat.

"Look at you!" said Doris when she came home for the weekend. "Aren't you smart? I bet you will have the ladies falling all over you, brother!"

Not for the first time Alice wondered where that little boy, who had played in the garden at Redhill, had gone.

"If they were I would not be telling you Doris" laughed Stan. "Though, to tell you the truth" he said seriously, "I have not

Stanley.

really come across anybody that I could fall for just yet."

"Now then Doris" chided Alice "plenty of time, plenty of time, good gracious me the lad is not even nineteen yet."

She packed him up some cake to take back to camp with him and, as usual, the little group of people stood and watched as he boarded the bus to take him back to the station and then on to where he was stationed. He was happy though, and because he was happy, so were they.

◆ ◆ ◆

CHARLES COULD NOT HAVE been more contented. This was the longest he had been anywhere since starting at Althorp House and it looked like he would be here to stay. There was nothing he enjoyed more than to get up in the morning and go out and feed his chickens and then stride off to the gardens and do a days work there. Quite often Mr. Gabriel would come out and talk to him. Despite their different backgrounds they had empathy towards each other because they had children of much the same age. Christopher Gabriel also had great respect for Charles's ability as a gardener and his skills at propagation of plants and topiary. He was very mindful of the sort of establishments where his gardener had worked as a young man. In fact Charles was the Head Gardener in all but name. As a family the Gabriel's were nothing, if not, loyal and Alfred had all the respect he deserved and would remain in the larger Coxhill Lodge for as long as he wanted.

Although modest, by Easthampstead standards, Coxhill Manor was still a large estate and so there were also half a dozen younger men who learned from Charles and Alfred. There was also the farm to be taken care of and which was now being taken over by Mr. Gabriel's son Ralph.

It was quite common for Mr. Gabriel to call at Covent Garden, whilst he was up in London, or to a Nursery Garden and purchase some exotic rose or lily that had just been discovered and then bring it back for Charles to propagate.

"Here you are Ratcliff, try this one!" he would say "see what you can make of this." He would present Charles with something that looked like nothing more than a stick with a few roots and expect flowers on it by the end of the year. More often than not he was able to oblige.

It was a glorious summer's day and Charles with the help of one of the younger gardeners was busy putting up the bean poles. It wasn't long before Mr. Gabriel came over and started chatting. He was a tall imposing man and today he was wearing his tweed suit and brown leather boots.

"Good morning Ratcliff, good morning Burton" He always made a point of calling Charles by his surname in front of the juniors but when they were on their own it was Christian names, except that Charles would never dream of calling him Christopher. He would always be Mr. Gabriel and the children would always be 'master' or 'miss'.

"Good morning Mr. Gabriel" replied Charles "nice one today."

"How is your boy Stan doing?" said his employer. "Is he still enjoying the RAF?"

"Oh he loves it. It is certainly making a man out of the boy."

"Yes I daresay it is" replied Christopher Gabriel. "You know my boy John is going in the Army?"

Charles had a feeling of foreboding but tried to hide it.

"I know" he went on "I know what you went through, but it is a different world now."

"It certainly is Mr. Gabriel."

"Anyway, I'll let you get on with things." He went to take his leave and stepped back onto the path taking the mud from his boots with him. "I've been looking round the front" he said as he stamped the mud from off of his feet. "My wife says she would like a rose garden round there."

"I'll see what I can find for you down the road at the Nursery" said Charles.

"Yes, you do that" he smiled. "Maybe some nice red and white ones would be nice."

He strode off leaving all his mud behind but Charles was used to it.

"Ha ha young Burton" he laughed "it looks as though Mr. Gabriel has left you some muddy boot droppings to sweep up from the path."

"Darn him" said Burton "he is a nice old cove though."

"Yes, they are both very good employers Burton and I am afraid they are a dying breed" said Charles as they walked back to the greenhouse and he handed the boy the bass broom, "a dying breed and it's a shame. They can criticize the gentry but I have never had one who has done me down yet."

They stopped at the sound of aircraft flying overhead. They were coming from the nearby private airfield of Fairoaks, but also now, there were more and more coming from Farnborough and from the new aerodrome which was being built on one hundred and forty eight acres of land near Heathrow in Middlesex.

"It's becoming a common sight now" said Burton.

"Yes" replied Charles "I come from an era where the only thing we saw in the sky was a bird or the occasional balloon."

"I do think the RAF is the thing of the future," replied Burton as he collected the broom. "I envy your son."

◆ ◆ ◆

OCCASIONALLY THROUGHOUT THE FOLLOWING summer one could hear the tell tale noise of the airship being tested as it came over Chobham. It was an awesome sight. Then disaster! On 5th October 1930, in the same year that Heathrow Airport became operational, came news that the R101 had crashed on its maiden flight going over France, and all forty-eight passengers had been killed. Charles listened intently to the news on the wireless.

"Oh drat it" he gasped and thumped the table. "What a terrible thing Kate. What a terrible thing."

It was all over the papers. All the bodies were carefully put on a ship and Stanley was chosen to be among the RAF Guard of Honour to fetch them by train from Dover to London. The Secretary of State for Air was among the dead.

Of course Charles and Alice listened to all the reports of the funeral service and the parade and saw the pictures in the paper but that was nothing like the first hand account that they got from their son when he came home on leave.

"Oh you should have seen it" said Stanley "to see those forty-eight coffins all being brought back and then the crowds lining the route, it was just a magnificent sight for such a sad occasion. And such crowds, I have never seen such crowds of people all lining the route."

"Well I don't think the airships will ever be suitable for passengers," said Alice. "I wouldn't want to go in one."

"Oh I don't know Mother" replied Stan "think of the view you would get."

Charles stayed silent. He had seen airships being used for something very different.

It had been a dreadful cloud on an otherwise enjoyable time in the RAF, but even though the event was a sad one and just terrible for all the families of the victims, Stan felt a surge of pride that he had been among those that had escorted them home. He loved the RAF life but he had signed on for six years. Once that was done he would probably have to come out and then be in the Reserves. He would use the skills he had learned in the air force to do a civilian job that involved driving and perhaps he would take a wife and settle down. Nobody could ever imagine that already the German Nazi Party was rising to power just as his uncles had feared, and, at its head, one Adolf Hitler. Nor did he think, for one minute, as he cuddled little Edie before going back to camp that she would be gone less than a year later.

◆ ◆ ◆

LITTLE EDIE DIED IN June 1931. As the doctor had said, eleven years ago, she would be prone to getting illnesses and not be able to fight them off. Alice rushed her to see the doctor as soon as she realised a cold and cough she had was not getting any better. What started off as 'bronchial trouble' eventually turned to pneumonia. No matter what anyone did, and how often Doctor Legg came to visit, or how much care the hospital gave, the end was inevitable. Everybody in the family were beside themselves with grief. Even Mr. and Mrs. Gabriel were upset.

"Oh you must stop at home with Alice" said Mrs. Elsie Gabriel when Charles called at the Manor and told her the news. The tears streamed down her face which made him feel worse.

"Thank you madam" he grunted.

"Come" she said "come and sit down and have a sherry."

He followed her into the Drawing Room and they were joined by Mr. Gabriel who patted Charles on the back.

"So sorry Charles, so very, very sorry old chap."

Charles drunk his sherry to be polite but all he wanted to do was to get back to Alice and then get stuck into his work. He could take his rage out with the pruning shears on the hedge down the back Drive. He politely took his leave of them and Mr. Gabriel patted him on the back.

"If there is anything we can do just say."

"Thank you Sir" grunted Charles. He was determined not to shed a tear in front of anyone.

Little Edie,

Doris got time off from her job and Stanley managed to get compassionate leave. He was now stationed at Uxbridge so it wasn't too far. A telegram was sent to Rosa and she came rushing home from Jersey. She was totally distraught.

"Well she will be with the angels in heaven now" said Alice who was absolutely staunch in her beliefs. Equally, Charles, with his Salvation Army background, was convinced that she was in heaven and that she was in God's hands.

"I'm not so sure" grunted Stanley to himself "otherwise why would she be taken from us so soon? It's not fair."

The funeral took place in St. Lawrence Church, Chobham and the building was packed. She was buried in the children's part of the Cemetery underneath an overhanging Yew tree. It was a beautiful day and the birds were singing. The grave was a mound of flowers from the people of the village and from the family.

Afterwards the immediate family went back to the house and squashed in somehow into the little kitchen and overflowed out into the garden. Mr. and Mrs. Mumford came across with their daughter Edna who, at eleven, was growing fast and was much the same age as Edie would have been.

"Such a shame" said Doris Mumford, "she was such a sweet girl."

Alice busied herself making tea and handing out cakes. She was all right as long as she could remain busy but she did not look forward to the place being empty again.

It was inevitable though, and one by one, everybody took their leave. Only Stan, Doris and Rosa remained and they had to go back to their respective jobs in the morning.

Alice gave them all a good breakfast and then, as they always did, she and Charles stood at the gate to watch the young people get on the bus to Woking. Doris would be going to her job on the outskirts of the town. Rosa would be getting the train that would eventually take her to the ferry and St. Aubin on Jersey. Stanley was en route back to Uxbridge.

"You know it is Rosa that has surprised me" said Charles as he comforted Alice and they strolled back indoors. "I never thought she had it in her to travel all that way on her own."

"She must get it from us dear" Alice smiled through her tears.

"Mind you, she is not there yet" said Charles. We could end up with a cable saying that she had ended up on the Isle of Wight."

He always had the knack of lightening the occasion.

Later, back in the quiet of his shed, Charles set about making the cross for the grave out of dark hard wood. It bore her name "Edith Joan Ratcliff" and the neatly painted words in white "suffer the little children to come unto me." The family motto may have been "if you can't make it or grow it then it's not worth having" but this was a labour of love.

◆ ◆ ◆

ROSA HAD NOT BEEN back at St. Aubin for long when there was another death in the family. This time it was Edith's husband Wilfred.

"Edith is beside herself" wrote Rosa "she is talking about selling the 'Bon Viveur' and returning to live with Laney in

Mitcham. This, of course, means that I shall be coming home before long."

Alice read it with a cross between a heavy heart on behalf of Edith but relieved that it meant that Rosa would be coming home.

"Oh God forgive me for being so selfish" she said out loud, "but it feels so empty now that Edie is gone."

"It is just as well she is coming home" replied Charles as he sat down and devoured his bread and cheese. "I still think that it is too near to the French main land. Who knows what may happen in the future."

But still, Alice did feel for Edith. They had been so excited about opening the tea rooms.. It had come about because her brother Joshua had got himself involved with doing some architectural work in Jersey. He had furnished the builders with the designs for several houses along the Boulevard at St. Aubin. He met Wilfred and befriended him and, over time, introduced him to Edith. Alice had met him once or twice and thought he was a really nice chap. Then there was their daughter Joan, who was Rosa's age, so when Rosa had gone there to stay, it had all worked out very well. Now, it looked like it was all over.

"Well, at least the house will be a bit livelier now" said Alice.

"Mores the pity" joked Charles. "I was enjoying the peace and quiet."

"Oh don't tell fibs" she replied "you don't like an empty house any more than I do." Suddenly she thought of Little Edie again and her eyes welled up with tears. She brushed them away and busied herself with the washing up.

"I'll get her looking after the chickens" he said "maybe she can talk to that damned red hen and persuade her to lay some eggs or she will end up on our dinner table."

"Who?" said Alice wickedly, "the chicken or Rosa?"

Her sad thoughts ended in laughter. Once again Charles knew when to lighten the mood.

Rosa returned a month later and settled back at home. She went back to her job helping her father in the gardens of Coxhill Manor. She also helped to look after the chickens in the pen in their own garden. She didn't get the red hen to lay though and it did, eventually end up on the dinner table!

At the back of the house they had the big chicken run with half a dozen hens and a rooster. Though the rooster was on borrowed time every morning when it crowed.

"Dang thing! I'll wring it's neck yet!" he would cry. But, of course, he knew that without the rooster there would be no baby chicks, so that was that!

A day did not go by without them remembering little Edie and how she used to play in the yard and out in the field. Once a week Charles went to the Cemetery to put fresh flowers on the grave and, eventually, when the time was right, to plant the flowers that were in season, such a primroses and crocus in the spring, and lobelia and alyssum in the summer.

For Alice the worst thing was that she could now take the lid off the well. It wasn't needed any more.

PITSFORD 1937

THE SOUND OF SINGING filled the air in the village of Pitsford and the crowds spilled out of the little Church and into the churchyard. Everyone was joining in the music and the tambourines of the Salvation Army at the funeral of Elizabeth Ratcliff. Just two years ago they had been here to bury John, her husband. The music and the sounds of instruments rang all over the little village as they laid the Lacemaker to rest. All the family were there, John and Joseph and Mabel and their spouses and children.

"It's a job to recognise them all these days" whispered Alice. Stanley was standing next to her. He was no longer in the Royal Air Force. He had loved every minute of the time he had spent learning how to be a driver and mechanic and he had seen a bit of the countryside. He did have a 'bit of an itch' to sign on but, instead, stayed on the reserves. Now he was working for a firm locally and he had also bought himself a second hand motor cycle. He regretted hanging his uniform up though. He felt a slight twinge of jealousy towards John Gabriel, who had joined up in the Army at the same time as he had joined the RAF and was still there, but then he was an Officer and things were always going to be different for him.

"Ah, you have done the right thing my lad" said Charles when Stan voiced his regret. "I don't like what is going on in the world today. You are better off here."

It was true, there were storm clouds over Europe and, despite what his father had said, there was every possibility that he would get called up again. One never knew these days. He might not get any choice anyway, any more than his father did a generation before him.

He put his arm round his mother and gently patted Charles on the back as they walked out of the Church.

"Come on, Grandmother is at rest now."

"She was a good age" said Charles, "Eighty-one. I hope I do as well."

They all went back to the house and Emmie took on the job of making the tea for everyone.

"She was a clever old stick" said Joe as they sat around and chatted.

"It's a dying art though" said Joseph. "You don't see the lacemakers around any more. It's all done by machine now."

"It's a shame though" said Alice. "I still have that lovely bedspread that Mother made."

John and Elizabeth.

"It's awful to think that both Mother and Father have now gone" said John.

"And now we have a Coronation to look forward to" said Emmie, trying to lift the gloom, "now that Edward has abdicated and gone off with that Mrs. Simpson woman."

"Good job too" mumbled Charles "he was no better than he ought to be, I think the new King and that nice wife of his will be much better."

"Shame though" said Joseph "I'll bet old George the fifth is rolling in his grave at the idea of his son abdicating."

"Well I think the new King will have his work cut out" said Alice "I wonder if he will ever meet that man Hitler."

"I doubt that very much" said Mabel. "He is a dreadful man."

"Oh it will never be the same as the old days though" replied Alice. "The days of Victoria and all the fine clothes and the big houses like Easthampstead and Ringwood. Those were the days."

As usual at these functions, the younger members of the family disappeared into the garden where John's old penny-farthing bike was still propped up in the shed.

"Gosh, did our Granddad used to ride that?" laughed Doris.

"Blow that" said Stanley. "I think I would rather have my motor bike."

"You would have had fun riding a motor bike around the Channel Islands" said Rosa. "People can ride all around the Island all the time."

"I wonder who has got the tea rooms now" said Stanley.

Rosa shrugged her shoulders. She had no idea but she had memories of the place that she would never forget.

"It is certainly going to be strange in the village without Grandmother sitting outside the door making her lace" said Barry.

"Well, I suppose she was a good age," replied their cousin Valerie. "I agree though, we will all miss her."

Indoors the older generation were concerning themselves with the storm clouds brewing in Europe and elsewhere.

"Did you hear on the News?" said Emmie. "There is so much fighting between the Chinese and Japanese."

"Well at least that's too far away to affect us," said Joseph.

"Oh it's just awful," said Alice, "and what with this chap Hitler, I just can't bear the thought. It is becoming so that I don't want to read the news any more."

"You would think they would have all learned from the last time," said Charles.

"I know brother." said Joseph. "I just escaped it by being too old. I never thought I would be so glad to be too old."

"Well it is a jolly good job that the Yanks came in and helped us out," said Charles. "If they hadn't, I think Lord Kitchener would have been calling up fifty year olds."

"Anyway, lets have a toast to Pitsford's Lacemaker" said John "raise your glasses all of you. To Mother and let's hope she is happy making lace for the angels."

"To Mother!" they all responded.

All too soon the family had to depart and get the train back to Surrey. Both Elizabeth and John had been laid to rest, and Stanley had another good reason for being anxious to get back home. His sister Doris had introduced him to a rather nice young lady who he wanted to get to know a bit better...

CHAPTER XVI

Before the Rainbow, 1937

Every day now there were stories of Hitler's rise to power and dreadful massacres further afield in China. Charles listened to the News and nothing seemed to improve.

"You know Kate, they are saying that this man has got concentration camps for his political opponents. You know I think it is only a matter of time before Stanley is called back into the RAF again."

"Oh I do hope not" replied Alice, "though I do think he misses it, but he has been courting that nice girl Lily that works with Doris.

"Well Lily might have to be prepared to go through what we went through" he grunted.

Alice had taken to Lily straight away. Doris had brought her home from work with her. She 'lived in' as a Parlour Maid and just went home to her family at weekends. However, Doris persuaded her to come home to Coxhill one Sunday which turned out to be the turning point of her life.

"Come on, do come home and meet my family," Doris said. "My mother does a lovely roast lamb, and...and" Doris whispered mischievously, "you may meet my handsome brother."

Lily wasn't so sure but she was persuaded, even if only out of curiosity, and the two girls cycled to Chobham on their bicycles.

As it turned out she had a lovely day with the whole family finishing with a pleasant walk around the local area.

"What did you think of him?" said Doris as they were riding back along the road.

"Very nice" replied Lily "and very handsome."

It wasn't long before the bicycle was replaced by the pillion of Stanley's motorbike and he had been courting the pretty young girl from Woking ever since. At the same time Doris had fallen for the chauffeur that worked at the big house next door to where they worked.

The sound of a motor bike being brought up the path with the engine still on heralded the arrival of Stanley.

"I wish that boy would not do that" exclaimed Charles. "He never turns that damned engine off until he gets it right up to the back door."

The engine stopped and he strode in with Lily.

"I've just brought Lily home for tea" he said "it's her day off."

Alice leapt to her feet and gave Lily a kiss on the cheek while Stan took his gauntlets and boots off and sat down near the fire.

"Come in my dear and make yourself at home," she exclaimed ignoring her husband and his moans about Stanley's motor bike, "where is our Doris today?"

"Oh, I think she is going out to the cinema with Harry Turner" replied Lily "I believe there is a good Charlie Chaplin film on."

"Isn't the garden pretty" she continued, "I see you have done it all out in red, white and blue ready for the Coronation."

"Yes, I did think I was doing it for Edward" said Charles "but it seems it is for his brother instead."

Charles, who was a staunch Royalist, had planted the garden with white alyssum, blue lobelia and red salvia and he had done the same for Mr. Gabriel.

"I'm not so sure if it will all be out in time" he muttered "May is a bit early to expect them to be in full bloom."

"Well it's very nice anyway Mr. Ratcliff" said Lily. She went and helped Alice with the tea and sliced some bread while Charles turned the radio on for the News. It was all about the rise of the Nazi Party and the unrest in Germany, together with the plans for the forthcoming Coronation.

"Goodness me, it is all happening isn't it!" said Stan.

"Oh here is Rosa coming now" said Alice as she caught sight of her through the kitchen window and could see her crossing the field. "She has been up at the house today."

"Well Lily, you are privileged" laughed Stanley as Rosa came through the door, "nearly the whole family here at one time. Now that is a rarity."

"Hello Lily, Isn't it exciting" said Rosa as she came in and gave her and her brother a kiss on the cheek. "They have been doing the whole house out with red, white and blue ribbon for the Coronation and they have given everyone the whole day off so that we can listen to it on the wireless."

"Well, I am glad it is George" said Alice as they all sat round the table with Charles at the head. "I've always preferred him to that brother of his." She looked across at Stanley. "His father was crowned the year that you were born."

"Twenty-six years on the throne. Not bad eh!" replied Stan. "Well good luck to George the Sixth anyway."

"I think his wife is lovely" said Lily "there are pictures of her and the two little princesses in all the magazines and papers."

"It's certainly something to look forward to after all this talk of unrest in the world" replied Rosa.

The Coronation took place on 12th May 1937 and everyone sat glued to the wireless for most of the day to listen to the commentator describing the procession. The wireless was still in its infancy and this was the first really big broadcast by the BBC.

The whole family, including Lily and Doris sat around in the kitchen and listened as the new King gave his Coronation speech. Alice gingerly got up out of her seat to go and put the kettle on the stove.

"Shh Kate" hissed Charles "he is just about to start his speech."

"They say he has an awful stutter" said Doris "how on earth will he manage?"

"You will find out in a minute" said Stan.

"Quiet!" exclaimed Charles. Everyone sat silent and listened as the King's faltering words came through the wireless and into their kitchen.

"It is with a very full heart that I speak to you tonight. Never before has a newly crowned King been able to talk to all his peoples in their own homes on the day of the Coronation. The Queen and I will always keep in our hearts the inspiration of this day. May we ever be worthy of the goodwill which I am proud to think surrounds us at the outset of my reign."

Charles jumped to his feet. Let us get the sherry out Kate. "God save the King. God bless him."

One year later and the storm clouds over Europe got ever darker.

◆ ◆ ◆

IN MARCH 1938 GERMANY announced the annexation of Austria and each day the news on Charles old crystal wireless got worse. The younger members of the family tried to ignore it but it was the talk of the household whenever he went into the kitchen of Coxhill Manor to take in the vegetables and fruit to Cook.

"Oh I don't know where it will all end" she said "every day I listen and they tell of dreadful massacres in China and the Far East and then there is this Eye Tye chap, Mussolini, and as for that awful Hitler... well I just don't know."

"Well I think Stan will have to go back into the RAF" said Charles.

They were disturbed by the arrival of Ralph and Kit, now both strapping fine young men.

"Hello Cook" they chorused "got any biscuits."

She laughed. "Nothing changes does it Master Kit and Master Ralph."

They raided the biscuit tin and then went off happy.

"Look at them" she said as they strode off. "They should be at work."

"I expect they have got somebody doing it for them" laughed Charles. "Not like us eh Cook?"

Kit would normally have been at work helping his father run the Timber Firm at the London Docks and Ralph ran the Farm over at Deep Pool, a few hundred yards away.

"Oh well, I suppose they can do what they like" he said "I can't, not if I am to dig the trenches for the next crop of spuds before it starts raining."

By the time Charles had finished for the day the heavens had opened but it didn't worry him. He was overtaken crossing the field by Rosa who had been working in the house.

"Come on father, you will get wet."

"I won't melt my girl" replied Charles and he crossed the field to check his bees as usual.

"Come on my beauties, I want a nice lot of honey from you this year" he said.

One or two were buzzing around but it didn't worry him, he was used to it.

Alice had the tea on the table when he got in.

"Where's Stanley?" said Rosa "He is usually here by this time."

"Oh I think he had something very special to do" replied Alice knowingly. She had a little glint in her eye as if she knew something that nobody else did.

"You have got a secret Mother" giggled Rosa, "come on, tell us your secret."

They were interrupted by the familiar noise of the motorbike engine coming up the path.

"I wish he wouldn't do that" muttered Charles, knowing it was to no avail.

The engine stopped and a few seconds later Stan and Lily came in with wide grins on their faces. Lily was blushing. It didn't take much to guess what was coming next.

"I have been to Lily's father to ask for her hand in marriage" said Stan.

"Oh Stanley how wonderful." Alice and Rosa came rushing up to them and Charles turned the wireless off, even though it was the News.

"Well done my boy,"

"Oooh let me see the ring" cried Rosa "when did you get that? You kept it so secret?"

"Mother knew" giggled Stan.

Lily held out her hand and showed them all the shiny engagement ring with three diamond stones.

"Well, this calls for a drink" said Charles. "Get the sherry out Kate!"

"How did your family take it?" asked Rosa.

"They are really thrilled" replied Lily. "My mother is already talking about a new hat."

Lily came from a large family who lived in nearby Knaphill, right opposite the Inkerman Barracks where her own father was stationed before going off to the Great War. She was one of eight brothers and sisters, all younger than her. She had barely seen them grow up because she was sent into service as a Scullery Maid when she was fourteen, although she was a Parlour Maid now.

"Well you won't be short of bridesmaids" said Alice. "You will have plenty to choose from.

"I think Doris will be married before me" laughed Lily. "We have some saving to do."

The evening came to an end with Rosa, Charles and Alice standing, as usual, at the gate to wave to them as they drove down the road.

"Look at that thing he drives" said Charles when they walked back into the house. "I still think we were better off with horses."

"Oh father, you should move with the times" laughed Rosa. She looked at her mother walking down the path in front of them. She still wore the same long dress with lacy collar that was the fashion in 1910. It would be a task to get them to embrace the 1930s.

◆ ◆ ◆

THE MARCH OF HITLER and the stories from Europe would not go away. First he annexed Czechoslovakia, and in March 1938 he occupied Austria.

"Darn good job Rosa is not in the Channel Islands anymore" declared Charles. "That tyrant will be occupying them next. You see if he doesn't."

All the way through 1938 the news got worse and worse. The only thing to lighten the occasion was the marriage of Doris to Harry. It was a lovely occasion and Rosa and Lily were the bridesmaids.

"Pity our parents can't be here to see this" said Alice as they came out of Church and lined up for photographs.

"Well none of us can go on for ever" replied Charles.

Both Doris and Lily though, lived in fear of what the next twelve months would bring. There was talk of conscription and Stan was in the Reserves anyway. Harry Turner wasn't but It was becoming inevitable for everyone.

With Doris married, the plans went ahead for the marriage of Lily and Stan. As Doris was now a married lady it fell upon Rosa and Lily's sister Phyllis to be the grown up bridesmaids along with her little sister, ten year old Elsie. Lily's brother Harry would be best man. Alice, Rosa and Lily, between them set about making all the dresses. Lily's was of white satin, and the bridesmaids of organdie.

Meanwhile Stan continued to go to work for the transport company, but any minute expecting the call to return to wearing uniform again. There was continual talk of war and Mr. Chamberlain, the Prime Minister was taking trips to try and negotiate with Hitler.

"He's wasting his bloody time" snarled Charles when he heard about it on the News. He thumped the table and the spoons in the drawer rattled.

The date for the wedding was set for 16th September 1939 in St. John's Church at Knaphill. Everything was ready, dresses finished and cake made and Charles was organizing the flowers. He even had a suit as he had to have one for Doris's wedding. It was his first since his own nuptials in 1908. Then the postman arrived with the notification that they had all been dreading. Stan was instructed to report for duty back in the RAF on 25th August.

Lily was devastated.

"We knew it was going to happen," said Stan but I promise you we will get married on the due date. I will see the Commanding Officer as soon as I arrive."

There was just time for him to report to West Drayton and get issued with his uniform before he was called upon to help in the evacuation of people from the Channel Islands. The Germans hadn't invaded yet, but some people were volunteering to leave just to be on the safe side. Having been in the RAF before, he needed no training and was set to work straight away.

Not though, before he went to the Commanding Officer and begged to have a weekend pass to get married.

Stan breathed a sigh of relief when the Officer signed the precious piece of paper. Clearly he was a man of some sympathy.

"Thank you Sir" said Stan and saluted.

"That's all right airman" replied the Officer "Just don't be late back. I think we may have a war to fight."

On the 1st September a million German troops invaded Poland. How long before it would be the Channel Islands?

"Well that's it" said Charles when he heard the News. "It will be war for sure."

"Oh no, not again!" said Alice. It had been inevitable for over a year but she had hoped it would go away. It didn't. On the 3rd September, less than a fortnight before the planned wedding of Stan and Lily, Britain and France declared war on Germany.

For a while it looked as though the wedding would have to be cancelled. There seemed to be no chance of the RAF honouring Stan's weekend to get married now! He went and saw the Commanding Officer again.

"It's totally out of order as you know" said the C.O. "but you will be going to France on the 18th so I think we had better make an exception."

♦ ♦ ♦

THE WEDDING WAS LOVELY and Charles and Alice met Lily's parents and her brothers and sisters. It was a beautiful, if poignant service but everyone tried to put the war out of their mind. After all 'maybe it was just a storm in a teacup', 'maybe it would all be over in five minutes'. It had already been arranged that Lily would move into the cottage with her in-laws until the war was over and Stanley returned from France. She would be able to have Doris's old room.

"After all, you are our daughter now" said Alice, "and you are to call us Mother and Father". Lily was happy to do so. There was not a lot of room at Hyde Cottage, where her parents lived and she shared a room with her sisters, Phyllis and Elsie.

After the service everyone went back to Lily's home for the reception and there was a beautiful three tier cake that had been organized by her mother.

It was planned that the couple would go straight off on honeymoon to London but Lily would be coming back to the Gardener's Cottage on her own.

When the time came everyone waited while she went upstairs to change into her going away outfit. Looking stunning, she joined her new husband and followed everyone outside to the gate where they watched and waited for the taxi to arrive to take them to the station. This time, much to Charles's relief, Stan had been forced to leave his motor bike back at camp!

Rosa couldn't stop the tears as she hugged her brother. He looked so smart in his uniform.

"You just stay safe" she said.

"I've got it all to come too", said Doris as she hugged them both. "My Harry will have to report for duty as well. Lily and I will have to look after each other."

Alice, at this moment, felt every one of her sixty years of age. How could she have guessed, all those years ago when she and the children watched Charles stride down the road in his uniform, that she would be doing it again for her son and, just like last time, with a war raging on the other side of the Channel. This time though it was different. This time things had progressed and aeroplanes could travel with ease across the Channel and drop bombs anywhere. It was all very frightening.

Charles tried to keep a stiff upper lip as he patted his son on the back.

Phyllis, Harry, Elsie. Stan, Lily, Rosa.

"If I can survive the Somme you can survive this lot" he said. He turned to Lily and put his arm around her. "Remember my dear, after every dark cloud comes a rainbow."

They were words that Lily would remember for a very long time.

How could such a happy day have so many clouds.

"Here is the taxi coming" shouted Rosa.

They watched it trundle down the bumpy Lane towards them. Then there were more hugs and everyone, Lily's parents and brothers and sisters, Rosa with Doris and Harry, Alice and Charles, all watched as the couple got into the taxi.

The following week there was a little note in the local paper dated 22nd September:-

"Miss Lily Dorothy Gosley, daughter of Mr. and Mrs. H. Gosley of Hyde Cottage, Knaphill was married at St. John's Church on Saturday to Mr. Stanley Ratcliff, only son of Mr. and Mrs. C. Ratcliff of The Gardener's Cottage, Coxhill, Chobham.

The Reverend H.G. Edwards officiated and the best man was Mr. H. Gosley, brother of the bride.

Given away by her father, the bride was attired in an ankle length dress of white satin, with veil and orange blossom. She carried a bouquet of pink carnations. The bridesmaids were Miss Rosa Ratcliff, Phyllis Gosley and Elsie Gosley. The two adult attendants wore dresses of pink organdie and carried sheaves of gladioli.

A reception was held at the Bride's home. The bride and bridegroom afterwards left for London, the bride travelling in a camel hair coat with brown hat and shoes to match."

Carrying out his parent's motto to the letter Charles grew all the flowers for the bouquets and headdresses and arranged them all himself.

◆ ◆ ◆

Two months later Charles, Alice, Lily and Rosa walked in the late Autumn sunshine to the memorial in Chobham Village for the service of Remembrance. The stone edifice had been erected soon after the First World War and Charles and Alice went every year to remember the dead and to pray for the safe return of those fighting now. The place was packed and music was being provided by the Salvation Army Band. Charles thought straight away of his Mother and Father and all those where he had been brought up in Pitsford, including his friend Henry who had suffered so much at the hands of the Turks.

Stan managed to keep in touch with Lily by letter from France.

"Talk about 'history repeating itself' grunted Charles.

With all the carnage that was happening on a daily basis Lily was just glad that he was still alive and in one piece and she clung to Charles's words 'after every dark cloud comes a rainbow'.

The crowd was bigger than ever at the Memorial this year and they were joined by Mr. and Mrs. Gabriel and their daughter Enid.

"Hello Charles, Alice, Rosa!" said Mrs. Gabriel. She turned to Lily "Oh and this is the new daughter-in-law! I'm very pleased to meet you. Don't you worry my dear, your Stanley will come back safe."

As the Band played everyone was locked in their own thoughts. They were the thoughts of loved ones and the hopes that it would all be over soon. Little could anybody dream that it would go on for another six years and it was just as well!

♦ ♦ ♦

STAN WAS ABLE TO keep in touch by letter and exactly one year later, towards the end of the Battle of Britain, he was on his way home from France for a short leave before his next posting. The skies above southern England were filled with aircraft as the RAF tried to save us from certain invasion. Lily rushed back from work as she had received a letter to say that he would try to get home, and also because to travel anywhere these days was dangerous. Everything seemed to be happening at once what with the evacuation of our soldiers from Dunkirk and the Battle raging in the skies. You took your life in your hands every time you stepped out of the door and London was being bombed mercilessly. Lily now worked for Sainsbury's in Woking mainly because the money was better than that of a Parlour Maid and she wanted to help her mother and father-in-law towards her keep.

Rosa came running across the field, anxious to get indoors before any air raid sirens went off. Above the skies seemed to hum, as they had for the past couple of months, with the sound of the spitfires.

"We have come a long way since Frederick Cody" mused Charles, as he and Alice watched, fascinated and transfixed, at the sight above their heads. "Maybe this will sort those damn Krauts out."

They watched as the dog fights went on above and somewhere in the distance one of the planes, they couldn't tell which, came crashing down.

"Can you imagine what it must be like in London" said Rosa. "Can you imagine what it must be like for Aunt Laney and Aunt Edie?"

"She's right" said Charles. "I think we should let them come and live with us until it is all over. "It will be a squash but we will manage somehow. They can go in the big room with you Rosa."

Rosa didn't mind. She got on well with both her Aunts.

The sound of a siren sent them all flying indoors and under the kitchen table.

"This is what those barbarians have reduced us to" snarled Charles. "Wasn't once enough for them?"

"Oh God please make Stan be all right!" prayed Lily as the 'all clear' sounded and they emerged.

As if in answer to her prayers, suddenly there was the sound of a motor bike as it was being pushed along the path. This time Charles did not complain that his son did not switch the engine off. Everyone fell on Stan as he walked in the door.

"What a game I had getting home" said Stan "It was a nightmare dodging potholes and bits of aeroplane. I almost went in the ditch twice." He turned to his father. "I will have to leave the motor bike behind this time Dad, and go back to camp by train. He hugged Lily. "I'm afraid we are going to Malta by ship and goodness only knows when we will be back. The only consolation is that the RAF is knocking the Luftwaffe out of the skies."

Alice did what she always did in times of stress. She put the kettle on to boil while Lily tried, and failed, to hold back the tears.

She arranged to take time off work and the rest of the family tried to leave the young couple as much on their own as possible but it was only a few days and the time went by like lightening. All too soon it was time for Stan to put on his uniform, pack his kitbag and get the bus to the station and this time the motor bike stayed in the shed.

He gave his mother and father a big hug and kissed his sister.

"I will write to you as soon as I can. They say I can write as soon as I am on the ship and it will be delivered to you."

"You just take care of yourself my son" said Alice "we want you back in one piece."

They watched as Lily walked with Stan to the bus stop and then discreetly returned back to the house. Even Charles had a job to hold back the tears which were mingled with rage. Alice and Rosa could not help themselves.

"Now lets have none of that" said Charles gruffly "Lily will be back in a minute and we need to keep a stiff upper lip and give her some support."

The two women brushed their tears away just as a distraught Lily came into the house and flung herself into the chair. Little did any of them know that it would be two and a half years before they would see him again.

A few days later and the mood changed with the words of The Prime Minister Winston Churchill who was always guaranteed to lift the nation's spirits. Charles switched the wireless on and everyone gathered round to hear his speech following the great Battle of Britain. Alice clattered some cups in the sink.

"Shh Kate, listen" commanded Charles "its Winston Churchill." Everyone sat in silence.

"The gratitude of every home in our Island" said the Prime Minister "in our Empire, and indeed, throughout the world, except in the abodes of the guilty, goes out to the British airmen who, undaunted by odds, unwearied in their constant challenge and mortal danger, are turning the tide of the World War by their prowess and by their devotion. Never in the field of human conflict was so much owed by so many to so few. All hearts go out to the fighter pilots whose brilliant actions we see with our own eyes day after day, but we must never forget that night after night, month after month, our bomber squadrons travel far into Germany, find their targets in the darkness by the highest navigational skills, aim their attacks, often under the heaviest fire, often with serious loss, with deliberate careful discrimination and inflict shattering blows on the whole of the navigational and war making structure of the Nazi power. On no part of the Royal Air Force does the weight of the war fall more heavily than on the daylight bombers who will play an invaluable part in the case of invasion."

"Well, if that doesn't stir the soul nothing will" said Charles. "God bless the Prime Minister."

A few days later Aunts Laney and Edith moved into the bungalow.

11TH NOVEMBER 1940

A FEW WEEKS AFTER the Battle of Britain and the Evacuation from Dunkirk the inhabitants of the Gardener's Cottage were at the Memorial in the Village again.

Lily had received a letter from Stan which was written on board ship.

"There has been a lot of waiting around but we should be leaving soon" he wrote.

Just over one year on from the outbreak of the 2nd World War everyone had their own reasons to pray fervently and to have their own thoughts during the two minutes silence.

After the service they were, as usual, joined by Mr. and Mrs. Gabriel.

"It was a good job you did on those roses in the front garden" said Mr. Gabriel. "They are a splendid sight Charles."

"Oh I was well taught when I was at Belton House up in Lincolnshire" replied Charles. He had a sudden memory of his friend Henry and his manure.

"Have you heard from Stanley?" said Mrs. Gabriel as they all walked down the road in the sunshine.

"Yes" said Lily "he has arrived in Malta. He has been promoted and he is a Sergeant now."

"Well the RAF did a good job over our skies in the last few months" said Christopher Gabriel, "but I fear we have a long way to go to stop invasion. They are even forming a Home Guard now for men who are older and retired as a last resort if the Germans do invade. I believe they are forming one in the village."

That cheered Charles up. He wanted to do his bit too. He felt so helpless and wished he could take on the whole of the German Army and kick their insides out.

"That sounds like a good idea to me Sir" he said "I think I shall join.

All the women tried hard to hide their smiles.

"I'll tell you something" whispered Alice "I wouldn't want to be any German that came across him!"

The sound of a siren sent them all scurrying to the air raid shelter in the grounds of the Manor.

Later that week Charles reported to the Home Guard in the village and volunteered his services.

Rosa and Lily stood at the gate and watched as Charles cycled down the road in his recently issued uniform. It wasn't the first time for Rosa. She had only been a small child when he had gone off to the First World War and she had waited and waited for him to come back. This time though it was slightly different. This time she found it hard to suppress a grin. But her father meant business and her mother was right. God help any German that he came across! He would take no prisoners!

Lily had another reason to smile. She had reason to believe she was pregnant.

◆ ◆ ◆

CHARLES AND ALICE STOOD in the back garden of the Gardener's Cottage and looked across toward the farm that was run by Mr. Gabriel's son Ralph. It was getting very cold and there had just been a sharp burst of rain but the sun was just coming out from behind the clouds. News had just been received up at the Manor that Mr. and Mrs. Gabriel's son John, a Captain in the Army, had been killed on board the SS Jonathon Holt two hundred miles off the North West coast of Scotland. The ship had been torpedoed by an enemy submarine.

"What the devil was he doing on a ship near the Artic" said Charles as he put his arm around Alice and held her close.

"I don't think the Gabriel family know or care" said Alice "all they know is that they have lost their son. How many more mothers are to lose sons before we are done. How many mothers lost their sons in the last lot? Surely after thousands of years of civilization they can start to get it right."

They stood together and slowly a rainbow formed over the farm.

"There you are" said Charles "there's the sign. There's the sign that says that everything *will* be all right in the end." He hugged Alice to his side. "it will be Kate. Stanley will be home

'Dad's Army'.

and we *will* all live happily ever after." But Charles had been listening to the News and he knew that Malta was, at that very moment, receiving a battering like no other as the enemy attempted to take this strategic little Island and the allies fought back.

Their thoughts were interrupted by a cry from the house. "Mother, Father, the kettles on and tea is ready." It was Lily. She had taken time off work to go to the Doctor and she had some news for them.

◆ ◆ ◆

THE FOLLOWING JUNE 1941, as the Siege of Malta continued and the bombs were raining down on Stan at RAF Luqa, Lily gave birth to a little girl. A telegram was immediately sent to him but they had no way of knowing whether he got it or not.

As far as Charles and Alice were concerned their lives were almost complete. But they, and millions like them, would have to wait another four years for their loved ones to return safe and sound.

As Alice nursed her grandchild in her arms she thought back to the day when she had first met Charles when he had played the accordion at Easthampstead. She still wondered if he would ever be induced to play it again.

"Maybe" she muttered to the baby under her breath, "just maybe when your Daddy comes home safe. Maybe *then* he will play that old squeezebox."

"Pardon Kate!" said Charles.

"No matter" she replied "no matter,"

Lily looked up from her sewing just in time to catch the smile that crossed Alice's face.

Charles gave Alice a peck on the cheek and lifted himself out of his chair just as Rosa arrived home. She was dressed in the uniform of an Auxiliary Nurse.

"There you are everyone" laughed Charles "even Rosa is doing her bit." He walked towards the bedroom. "Anyway, it's time for me to get changed and go and do my duty. You ladies had better pull the black out curtains. I don't want any bloomin' ARP chap telling me we have any chinks of light showing."

He emerged ten minutes later in his Home Guard uniform. "Woe betide any bloody German that comes near me" he grunted.

Alice carefully put her grandchild into the crib and the three women watched as he slung his rifle across his back and went off down the road on his bike.

"The Germans have no chance!" laughed Alice.

It would be another four more years, but Alice was right. Alice was always right.

THE END

Charles and Alice.

Epilogue

D id Stanley and Harry get home safely after the war? Did Charles and Alice ever get to move into Coxhill Lodge? Did he ever find cause to play that accordion again? What was it like for a little girl whose early life was divided between long spells with a father missing and then following him around to wherever he was posted? Did everyone eventually live happily ever after?

The story of what happened to Alice and Charles next and the story of Stan and Lily's war, and eventual peace, is told in *Granddad's Rainbow*.

ALSO BY JOAN BLACKBURN

ALSO BY JOAN BLACKBURN

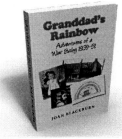

GRANDDAD'S RAINBOW
Adventures of a War Baby 1939 – 1951

IT IS 1944 AND three-year-old Joannie listens to the tall stories told by her Granddad as he tries to bring normality to a very abnormal time. Born into an upstairs/downstairs world that is fast becoming history, her grandfather, the Head Gardener at Coxhill Manor, near Chobham in Surrey, had seen it all before in 'the first lot'. Now his son, serving in the RAF in France and Malta, is just a face in a photograph to little Joannie, who one day will follow in her father's footsteps and join the Royal Air Force.

Joan Blackburn has returned, in this, her second book, to her rural working-class roots. With access to her father's RAF Record of Service and an Aunt who lived to be over 100 years old, together with the aid of her own memories, she has been able to piece together the events contained in the book accurately and informatively to create a create a realistic and warm-hearted portrayal of the life of an ordinary English family caught up in the extraordinary events of World War II and its aftermath.

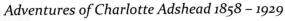

THE TAILOR'S DAUGHTER
Adventures of Charlotte Adshead 1858 – 1929

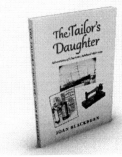

THIS IS THE TRUE story of the author's great-grandmother. Born in the 1850s in Clapham, London, she emigrated on her own to New Zealand at a time when to do such a thing was fraught with danger. It is also the story of Frederick Gosley, the seafarer whose life changed when he met Charlotte. It changed even more when he went blind and it took all the willpower and tenacity the plucky Cockney girl had been born with to overcome the difficulties that were to follow.

The book follows the couple through the years of their lives, which included events ranging from the sinking of the Titanic, the devastating First World War and Votes for Women until their deaths in 1929, within a few months of each other. From Charlotte's father Thomas to her Granddaughter, Lily Dorothy, it traces over a century of history.

The conversations are of necessity imagined but the facts and most of the people (including the passengers on the SS *British King*, on which Charlotte sailed to New Zealand) are real. Only a few minor fictional characters were added for the purposes of continuity.

NAAFI, KNICKERS & NIJMEGEN
Adventures of a WRAF Airwoman 1959-63

IT IS 1959 AND a teenage junior clerk joins the WRAF following a bet with her Father. What follows is a journey from the innocence of the austere fifties to the birth of the colourful sixties.

Beginning with the first tottering steps on a parade ground through to the adventure of going abroad and taking part in the 100-mile Nijmegen March three years later, it is a snapshot of the time.

Originally written in 1964, it is honest, accurate and not distorted by the passing of the years, but enhanced with the advantage of hindsight.

It shows ~ as only something written at the time can show ~ how gradually things changed, both in the WRAF and in civilian life, during that special, innocent time just before the sixties came of age.

Both informative and, at times, hilarious, it is a must for anyone who 'was there', whether they were in the services or not. At the same time, it offers a peep into 'another world' for anyone too young to have been there.

NAAFI, NIJMEGEN & THE PATH TO NORWAY

Further Adventures of a WRAF Airwoman –
1971 and beyond...

IT IS 1971 AND a secretary, who is nearer thirty than she wants to be, decides to return to the WRAF, to which she had said goodbye back in 1963. As this sequel to *Naafi, Knickers & Nijmegen* begins she reflects on her activities during the past decade and agonises over what to do next.

What will it be like to go back a second time and, perhaps, come across familiar faces, both welcome and unwelcome? What did she do in the intervening years and how will she adjust to being the 'old lady' to the teenagers as they join up for the first time in a WRAF which was already changing? Will she do the Nijmegen March again and maybe meet a man to change her life?

For those who have read the original book, which was written in 1964 but not published until 2009, this sequel written in 2015, answers all those questions and more. For others it is a window on life in the WRAF at a time when the world was a much more innocent place than it is now and a look at how things started to change.

It is not about being 'at the sharp end' or exploits of 'derring-do'. It's about having Air Force blue blood that never goes away, and passes from generation to generation. It also shows how life can be a series of circles.

Most of the names are real but one or two have been changed (to protect the guilty!).

All books published by Woodfield @ £9.95
www.woodfieldpublishing.co.uk
www.amazon.co.uk/shops/woodfield

About the Author

Joan Blackburn was born in Woking in 1941. Her first book 'Naafi, Knickers & Nijmegen' was published in 2009 and told of her adventures in the WRAF between 1959 and 1963.

After the success of this tale of Air Force life in the swinging sixties, Joan was encouraged to go back a generation for her second book 'Granddad's Rainbow'. This told of life on the home front both during and immediately after the war and featured her parents, Lily and Stan. It is against the, fast disappearing, upstairs/ downstairs life of her grandparents where they worked for the gentry and also against the background of Stan's life in the RAF serving in France and Malta and the steadfastness of Lily as she waited for him to come home.

In 'The Tailor's Daughter' Joan went back still further to the Victorian life of her Great Grandmother on Lily's side of the family, who, in the 1880s set sail for New Zealand on her own. Lily's maiden name was Gosley. Her grandfather married the plucky Charlotte Adshead and the decision they were forced to make, soon after their marriage, affected every generation thereafter. This trilogy of books cover 150 years of family history.

Joan is married to Norman Blackburn and lives in West Sussex. She has two children, Catherine and David, and five small grandchildren, Jacob, Alice, Lydia, Harvey and Keira.

◆ ◆ ◆